Flood Estimation Handbook

Volume 2

Flood Estimation Handbook

Volume 2
Rainfall frequency estimation

Duncan Faulkner

Institute of Hydrology

© NERC (CEH) 2008

ISBN for complete set of 5 volumes: 978-1-906698-00-3
ISBN for this volume: 978-1-906698-02-7

Originally published by the Institute of Hydrology 1999

Centre for Ecology & Hydrology

Maclean Building, Benson Lane, Crowmarsh Gifford
Wallingford, Oxfordshire OX10 8BB
UK

General and business enquiries: 01491 692562
E-mail: enquiries@ceh.ac.uk
Website: www.ceh.ac.uk

Cover photo: David Mould

Cross-referencing

Cross-references to other parts of the Handbook are usually abbreviated. They are indicated by the relevant volume number preceding the chapter, section or sub-section number, with the volume number in bold (e.g. **4** 2.2 refers to Section 2.2 of Volume 4). Cross-references conventionally prefixed by Chapter, Section or § are to the current volume.

The Flood Estimation Handbook should be cited as:
Institute of Hydrology (1999) Flood Estimation Handbook (five volumes).
Centre for Ecology & Hydrology.

This volume should be cited as:
Faulkner, D. S. (1999) Rainfall frequency estimation. Volume 2 of the Flood Estimation Handbook. Centre for Ecology & Hydrology.

Contents

Preface

The research for the Flood Estimation Handbook was undertaken at the Institute of Hydrology, Wallingford, Oxfordshire. The Institute is an integral part of the Centre for Ecology and Hydrology, and a component institute of the Natural Environment Research Council. The research programme ran from 1994 to 1999.

Contributors

The core research team comprised Duncan Reed (team leader), Adrian Bayliss, Duncan Faulkner, Helen Houghton-Carr, Dörte Jakob, David Marshall, Alice Robson and Lisa Stewart. David Jones acted as an internal consultant, advising on all aspects of the research. The WINFAP-FEH software package was principally developed by Lawrence Beran, and the FEH CD-ROM was designed and developed by Kevin Black. The Handbook is dedicated in memory of Tanya Jones, a team member whose contribution to hydrological research was tragically cut short by cancer.

Major contributions were also made by David Morris, Susan Morris, Christel Prudhomme and Robert Scarrott, with additional contributions by Val Bronsdon, Victoria Edmunds, Beate Gannon, Stephanie Hills and Nick Reynard.

The team was supported by 1-year Sandwich Course Students from Luton and Sheffield Hallam Universities, including: Mark Bennett, Robert Brookes, Russell Brown, Louisa Coles, Nick Davie, Philip Davies, David Hewertson, Catriona Kelly, Marina Syed Mansor and Paul Nihell.

Sponsors

The research programme was funded by the Ministry of Agriculture Fisheries and Food (MAFF), the Environment Agency, the Department of Agriculture Northern Ireland, and a consortium led by the Scottish Office. The budget for the programme totalled about £1.7m. Indirect support was provided by the Centre for Ecology and Hydrology, the Meteorological Office and river gauging authorities. Costs of final editing and publication of the Handbook, and development of the WINFAP-FEH software, were met by the Institute of Hydrology.

Advisers

The research was reviewed by the Flood Estimation Handbook Advisory Group, comprising:

David Richardson, MAFF Flood and Coastal Defence *(Chair)*
Linda Aucott, Environment Agency
Alan Burdekin, Scottish Office
John Clarke, Department of Agriculture, Northern Ireland
Christopher Collier, University of Salford
Conleth Cunnane, University College Galway, Ireland
John Goudie, MAFF Flood and Coastal Defence *(Technical Secretary)*
Richard Harpin, Sir William Halcrow and Partners
David MacDonald, Binnie Black and Veatch
Andrew Pepper, Consultant to the Environment Agency *(Observer)*
Duncan Reed, Institute of Hydrology
Richard Tabony, Meteorological Office
Howard Wheater, Imperial College

Testers

The main participants in the user test programme were:

David Archer, Consultant to Jeremy Benn Associates
Alan Barr and Grace Glasgow, Kirk McClure and Morton
Don Burn, University of Waterloo, Canada
Jonathan Cooper, Owen Bramwell and Brian Darling, WS Atkins North West
Con Cunnane and Savithri Senaratne, University College Galway
Steve Dunthorne, Sir Alexander Gibb and Partners
Jim Findlay, Murray Dale, Stuart King and Birol Sokmenor, Babtie Group
Mark Futter, Montgomery Watson
Malcolm MacConnachie, Scottish Environment Protection Agency
David MacDonald, Binnie, Black and Veatch
Ian Rose, Emma Blunden and Rob Scarrott, Halcrow
Peter Spencer and David Rylands, Environment Agency
Peter Walsh, Bullen Consultants Ltd
Paul Webster and Anna Lisa Vetere Arellano, University of Birmingham
Howard Wheater and Christian Onof, Imperial College

Acknowledgements

The Flood Estimation Handbook is a product of strategic research funding at the Institute of Hydrology in the 1990s. It would not have happened without the lead shown by MAFF, in particular by Reg Purnell and David Richardson. The dedication of Advisory Group members and the testers is gratefully acknowledged. Alan Gustard (IH) is thanked for managerial assistance in a research programme that did not fit a standard mould.

General thanks go to all those who exchanged ideas with members of the team during the research programme. Those having greatest impact on the course of the research were Don Burn and Jon Hosking. A more general acknowledgement is to all earlier researchers in UK rainfall and flood frequency estimation. It would be invidious to list some and not others.

Coastlines, rivers and lake shorelines shown in the Handbook are based on material licensed from Ordnance Survey and are included with the permission of the controller of Her Majesty's Stationery Office © Crown copyright. Place names are from a gazetteer licensed from AA Developments Ltd.

More specific acknowledgements to individuals and organisations co-operating in the research are made in the relevant volume.

Volumes

1 Overview
2 Rainfall frequency estimation
3 Statistical procedures for flood frequency estimation
4 Restatement and application of the *Flood Studies Report* rainfall-runoff method
5 Catchment descriptors

Notation

The following are the main symbols and abbreviations used throughout this volume of the Flood Estimation Handbook. Other symbols have just a local meaning and are defined where they occur. All the units are metric unless otherwise stated.

AM	Annual maximum
ARF	Areal reduction factor
BAR	Average distance to topographic barrier (km)
CWI	Catchment wetness index
D	Duration (hours)
DANI	Department of Agriculture, Northern Ireland
DDF	Depth-duration-frequency
DLILLE	Index of continentality: distance from Lille (km)
DTM	Digital terrain model
EA	Environment Agency
ELEV10	Average elevation (m)
F	Non-exceedance probability
FEH	Flood Estimation Handbook
FORGEX	Focused rainfall growth curve extension
FSR	Flood Studies Report
FSSR	Flood Studies Supplementary Report
GCM	General Circulation Model
ICE	Institution of Civil Engineers
IH	Institute of Hydrology
Met. Office	Meteorological Office
M5	5-year return period rainfall (mm)
N_e	effective number of independent gauges in a network
NERC	Natural Environment Research Council
OBST	Average angle of topographic obstruction
PEPR	Precision Encoder and Pattern Recognition
PMP	Probable maximum precipitation
POT	Peak over threshold
R	Rainfall (mm)
r^2	Percentage of variance explained
RMED	Median annual maximum rainfall (mm)
RMEDDY	Interpolated median annual maximum 1-day rainfall
$SAAR_{4170}$	Standard-period average annual rainfall, for 1941-70 (mm)
SEA	Average distance from the sea (km)
SEPA	Scottish Environment Protection Agency
T	Return period (years)
TBR	Tipping bucket recorder
TSR	Tilting syphon recorder
x	Standardised rainfall
y	Gumbel reduced variate

Chapter 1   Introduction

1.1 Overview

This Volume of the Flood Estimation Handbook introduces new procedures for estimating rainfall frequency in the UK. The depth-duration-frequency model described enables the estimation of extreme rainfalls at any location. The handbook is accompanied by a CD-ROM which provides the parameters of the model on a 1-km grid, and software which calculates estimates of design rainfall or event rarity. As well as explaining the use of the model, this volume describes the underlying research methods and results.

This volume deals with rainfall frequency alone, thus it does not include any advice on estimating probable maximum precipitation or snowmelt. For these topics, refer to Volume 4, Chapter 4.

Part A explains the rainfall frequency estimation procedures. It gives a brief guide to the depth-duration-frequency model and also describes the derivation of rainfall profiles for use in rainfall-runoff modelling. It includes a review of research on areal reduction factors and rainfall profiles, two topics not revisited in the FEH research programme.

Part B gives several worked examples to illustrate the use of the FEH rainfall procedures.

Part C is a detailed account of the underlying research, which was based on an analysis of annual maximum rainfalls. It includes the mapping of the index variable, the derivation of rainfall growth curves and the development of the depth-duration-frequency model. The results of the analysis are presented and discussed in the form of maps. Guidance is given on using the results in unusual situations.

Part D outlines the collection of rainfall data, summarises the database of annual maximum rainfalls and describes ten recent noteworthy storms.

1.2 Purpose of the procedures

The rainfall frequency procedures have two purposes: the estimation of design rainfall depths, and the assessment of the rarity of observed rainfall events.

Design rainfalls are required principally for river flood estimation, where they are an important component in the design of flood defences, bridges, culverts, balancing ponds and reservoir spillways. Many flood estimates depend on good rainfall frequency information because rainfall records tend to be more plentiful and longer than river flow records. Other applications for design rainfalls can be found in agriculture and in the design of sewerage for built-up areas and drainage for buildings.

Assessments of the rarity of observed rainfalls are useful for insurers, as well as being of interest to meteorologists, hydrologists and people affected by the events. Such calculations are also often important contributions to the assessment of flood rarity.

Chapter 2 describes how to obtain rainfall depths or rarity assessments at a single location. Because the procedures will frequently be used to provide a design rainfall depth for rainfall-runoff methods, Chapters 3 and 4 describe how to obtain catchment rainfall depths and how to choose a design storm profile.

1.3 Context

The FEH rainfall frequency procedure replaces the methods presented in Volume II of the *Flood Studies Report* (FSR). The FSR rainfall frequency results have been the basis of UK rainfall frequency estimation for more than 20 years and have had a worldwide influence. Although other local and regional studies of rainfall frequency have been published since then the FEH rainfall analysis is the first new nationwide study. Apart from incorporating an additional 25 years of data, this volume also addresses some of the weaknesses of the FSR analysis.

The FSR results have been described as over-general, masking important local and regional variations in rainfall frequency. Bootman and Willis (1981) expressed concern about the applicability of the FSR growth factors to Somerset and the surrounding region, demonstrating that the method seriously underestimates the magnitude of 2-day rainfalls. This was supported by Clark (1997) and Dales and Reed (1989), who also found that the FSR tends to underestimate rainfall in eastern England and overestimate in north-west England. Kelway (1975) and Reed and Stewart (1989) criticised the FSR method for failing to account for spatial dependence in rainfall extremes. Concerns about other aspects of the FSR rainfall method are mentioned in Chapters 3 and 4.

1.4 Outline of the analysis

The details of the analysis that led to the results presented in Part A are given in Part C. This short summary introduces the background to the depth-duration-frequency model. Figure 1.1 represents the analysis in a flowchart, and can be compared with Figure 1.2 which represents the FSR analysis. Both flowcharts distinguish between the underlying method and the work that is done by the user.

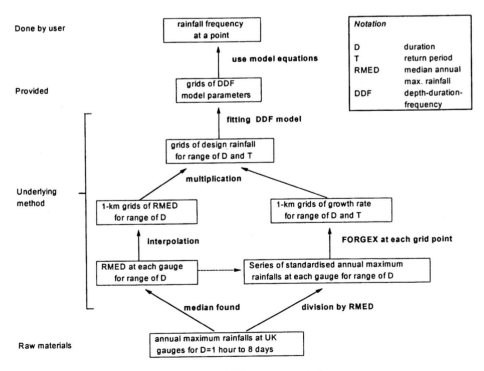

Figure 1.1 *Flowchart summary of FEH rainfall frequency analysis*

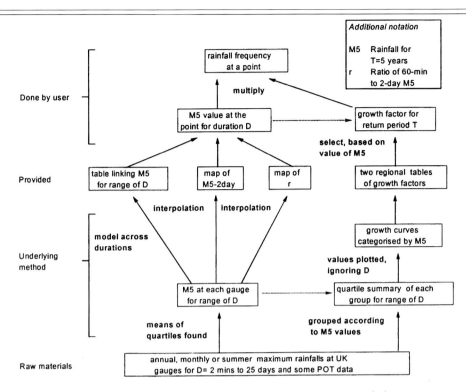

Figure 1.2 Flowchart summary of Flood Studies Report rainfall frequency analysis

The FEH rainfall frequency analysis is based on *annual maximum* rainfalls, which are the largest rainfalls observed in each year at a site. These are aggregated over various durations from 1 hour to 8 days. The two key parts to the analysis are the mapping of an *index variable* and the derivation of *growth curves*, which relate the rainfall depths of different return periods to the index rainfall. The index variable was chosen to be the median of annual maximum rainfalls at a site, RMED. Note that the index variable used in the FSR was the rainfall with a 5-year return period, M5. Values of RMED were interpolated between raingauge sites using topographic information, giving 1-km grids of RMED covering the UK.

Rainfall growth curves were derived by the FORGEX method, which was developed specifically for the study. The acronym FORGEX stands for FOcused Rainfall Growth curve EXtension. This was applied on a 1-km grid, and the resulting grids of growth rates multiplied by the grids of RMED to give design rainfalls. During the mapping of RMED and the derivation of growth curves, each rainfall duration was treated separately. The results were then incorporated into a model linking rainfall depth, duration and frequency (a DDF model), which was calibrated at each point on the grid. The parameters are supplied with the FEH, and the model is explained in the following chapter.

Chapter 2   Rainfall frequency at a point

2.1 Obtaining a design rainfall

The software accompanying the FEH enables the estimation of a design rainfall of any duration and return period for any location in the UK. The user need only supply the rainfall duration in hours, the return period in years and the grid reference in Great Britain or Northern Ireland to the nearest km. The program provides a design rainfall in mm, and can also display a plot of rainfall versus duration for several return periods. Worked examples are given in Chapter 5.

2.2 Assessing the rarity of an observed rainfall

The software also allows the estimation of the return period of a rainfall which has been observed at any location. In this case the user supplies the rainfall duration, the depth, and the grid reference. The program provides the return period of the rainfall event at that location. There is a worked example in Section 5.4, and further examples in Chapter 15.

2.3 The depth-duration-frequency model

The rainfall frequency estimates are calculated using a model of rainfall depth-duration-frequency (a *DDF model*). A detailed description and justification of the model can be found in Chapter 10; this section deals with the *application* of the model.

Terminology

The terms *return period, frequency* and *Gumbel reduced variate* all refer to the rarity of an event. The longer the *return period, T,* the rarer the event. See Section 2.4 for a formal definition.

Return periods should be viewed as probabilities rather than long-term predictions: there is a 0.0005 probability that the rainfall with return period 2000 years will be exceeded next year. Frequency, or *annual exceedance probability*, is the inverse of return period (on the annual maximum scale).

The *Gumbel reduced variate, y,* is defined so that the Gumbel frequency distribution (commonly used in frequency estimation) plots as a straight line when the horizontal axis has a reduced variate scale:

$$y = -\ln\left[-\ln\left(1 - \frac{1}{T}\right)\right] \qquad (2.1)$$

An example, for rainfall at Leicester in the English midlands, is shown in Figure 2.1. Rainfall duration in hours is shown on a logarithmic scale on the *x*-axis, and rainfall depth in mm on a logarithmic scale on the *y*-axis. Several lines are shown, each for a different return period. This diagram can be used to estimate design rainfalls for Leicester, or to estimate the return period of an observed rainfall.

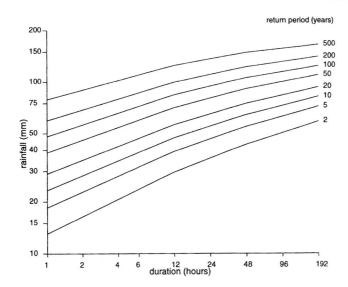

Figure 2.1 *DDF model for rainfall at Leicester*

A look at the parameters of the model is worthwhile at this point, as these are displayed by the software and quoted in the examples contained in the following chapters.

The lines on Figure 2.1 are defined by six parameters which control the slope and position of the lines and their variation with return period. The increase of rainfall with duration is represented by three concatenated line segments, with slopes a_1, a_2 and a_3. The intercept of the first segment on the rain axis where $ln\ D = 0$ is denoted b. Because the slopes and intercept vary with return period, and thus with the Gumbel reduced variate y, they should properly be denoted $a_1(y)$, $a_2(y)$, $a_3(y)$ and $b(y)$.

The form of the DDF model is shown on Figure 2.2, with two separate lines to illustrate the relationship with frequency. The breaks in slope are at durations of 12 and 48 hours (see §10.3.2).

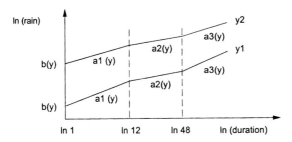

Figure 2.2 *Form of the DDF model*

The increase of rainfall with return period is represented by a change in the slopes and intercept with y. Figure 2.3 shows that a_1, a_2, and a_3 vary linearly with y according to the four parameters c, d_1, d_2 and d_3: $a_i = cy + d_i$. The parameter b varies linearly with y according to the two parameters e and f: $b = ey + f$. These six parameters (c, d_1, d_2, d_3, e and f) completely define the DDF model at any location.

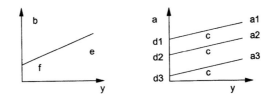

Figure 2.3 *Variation of the parameters a and b with Gumbel reduced variate, y*

The software reads the appropriate values of the parameters from the CD-ROM and then evaluates the design rainfall for duration D and Gumbel reduced variate y using the following formulae:

for $D \leq 12$ hours:

$$\ln R = (cy + d_1) \ln D + ey + f \qquad (2.2)$$

for $12 < D \leq 48$ hours:

$$\ln R = \ln R_{12} + (cy + d_2)(\ln D - \ln 12) \qquad [2.3]$$

for $D > 48$ hours:

$$\ln R = \ln R_{48} + (cy + d_3)(\ln D - \ln 48) \qquad [2.4]$$

The formulae are inverted to find the return period of an observed rainfall event, here given in terms of the Gumbel reduced variate y:

for $D \leq 12$ hours:

$$y = \frac{\ln R - f - d_1 \ln D}{c \ln D + e} \qquad [2.5]$$

for $12 \leq D \leq 48$ hours:

$$y = \frac{\ln R - f - d_1 \ln 12 + d_2 \ln 12 - \ln D}{c \ln D + e} \qquad [2.6]$$

for $D > 48$ hours:

$$y = \frac{\ln R - f - d_1 \ln 12 + d_2(\ln 12 - \ln 48) + d_3(\ln 48 - \ln D)}{c \ln D + e} \qquad [2.7]$$

The six parameters of the DDF model are defined for a 1-km grid covering the UK.

2.4 Validity of the DDF model

The model is fitted to design rainfalls aggregated over various durations from 1 hour to 8 days, and for various return periods up to 1000 years. The fitting is described more fully in Chapter 10. The model is designed to provide consistent estimates for return periods up to 10 000 years, although estimates for return periods this long are inevitably extrapolations. It should not be used for longer return periods, as there may be contradictions between estimates for different durations; indeed, the model is fitted with some constraints to avoid contradictions for return periods up to 10 000 years.

For very short return periods ($T \leq 1$ year), often required in analysing urban pollution events, the annual maximum scale is inappropriate, and the Gumbel reduced variate, y, is undefined. Any return periods shorter than 1 year must be measured on the peaks-over-threshold scale, which allows for more than one event per year. Extrapolated design rainfalls can be provided for a peaks-over-threshold return period, T_{POT}, by converting it into an annual maximum return period T_{AM}, using Langbein's formula (IH, 1977):

$$\frac{1}{T_{AM}} = 1 - \exp\left(-\frac{1}{T_{POT}}\right) \tag{2.8}$$

This formula ensures that $T_{AM} > 1$.

Return periods

The definitions of AM and POT return periods are:

T_{AM} is the mean interval between years containing one or more rainfalls above a given depth.

T_{POT} is the mean interval between rainfalls exceeding a given depth.

T_{POT} is always slightly smaller than T_{AM}, but the difference is relatively small for return periods over about ten years.

The range of rainfall durations to which the DDF model is fitted is 1 hour to 8 days. Some extrapolation beyond this range is justified, for example for durations as short as half an hour. The software makes clear when an answer is based on extrapolation. Such answers should be treated with less confidence. Further guidance on estimating short-duration rainfalls can be found in Chapter 12.

2.5 Discretisation

For most flood design applications, the required design rainfalls are aggregated over a duration that can start at any time. This is referred to as a *sliding* duration. In some cases, a rainfall frequency assessment is required for a *fixed* duration, which can start at discrete times only. An example would be the estimation of the return period of a 1-day rainfall total observed at a gauge which is read at 9 a.m. every day, or a 2-hour total observed at a gauge which accumulates hourly totals every clock hour.

The rainfall totals to which the DDF model is fitted are adjusted for this discretisation effect, so that the design rainfalls produced by the model are for sliding durations. The adjustment was made just before fitting the DDF model, as explained in Section 10.4.

The software includes an option to adjust rainfall depths to convert between fixed and sliding durations. Design rainfalls based on fixed durations are smaller than those based on sliding durations because a fixed period, say of one day, will rarely capture the highest 24-hour total in a rainfall event. The adjustment factors are taken from Dwyer and Reed (1995) and listed in Table 2.1. Rainfall depths observed over fixed durations are multiplied by these factors before an estimated return period is sought from the DDF model.

Table 2.1 *Factors used to convert fixed-duration to sliding-duration rainfalls*

Rainfall measured daily		Rainfall measured hourly	
Duration (days)	**Multiply by**	**Duration (hours)**	**Multiply by**
1	1.16	1	1.16
2	1.11	2	1.08
4	1.05	4	1.03
8	1.01	8	1.01
		≥12	1.00

Example 2.1

What is the rainfall for a range of durations with return period 100 years at Kirkintilloch, north of Glasgow? The grid reference of a site near Kirkintilloch is (264000 674000). The parameters of the DDF model at this point are:

c	d_1	d_2	d_3	e	f
− 0.015	0.432	0.400	0.359	0.241	2.303

The 100-year rainfalls for a range of durations are:

1 hour	7 hours	12 hours	1 day	4 days	8 days
30.3 mm	61.4 mm	74.7 mm	94.0 mm	144 mm	177 mm

All these rainfalls are for sliding durations. The rainfall for a fixed duration of 1 day — i.e. the depth which would be measured in a gauge read daily at 9 a.m. — can be estimated by adjusting for discretisation. The depth for a sliding duration of 1 day is divided by the appropriate factor from Table 2.1, which is 1.16, to give a 100-year rainfall of 81.0 mm for a fixed duration of 1 day.

Chapter 3   Rainfall frequency for a catchment

3.1 Requirement

For the rainfall-runoff method (Volume 4), or other models which estimate design floods from rainfall, a catchment rainfall total is required. This is obtained in two steps: first find a rainfall for a typical point in the catchment, then apply an areal reduction factor. The rainfall for a typical point in the catchment is found from parameters of the depth-duration-frequency model which are appropriate for the catchment. The areal reduction factor converts this point rainfall to an areal rainfall.

3.2 Catchment-average parameters of the DDF model

The catchment descriptor CD-ROM includes values of the six parameters of the rainfall DDF model for all UK catchments draining an area of at least 0.5 km². These are evaluated by taking a weighted average of point values, determined by overlaying the catchment boundary on the 1-km grid of parameters. The weights represent the proportion of the catchment falling within each 1-km grid square. Catchment boundaries are derived using the IH digital terrain model. More details are given in Section 10.6.

Example 3.1   [Please see special note on page 12]

The location near Kirkintilloch in Example 2.1 is in fact the site of a gauging station on the River Kelvin. The grid reference of the channel at the Dryfield gauging station is (263800 674000), and the catchment area is 235 km². It is now possible to estimate the design rainfall for a typical point in the catchment draining to this site. The catchment-average DDF parameters are:

c	d_1	d_2	d_3	e	f
– 0.016	0.430	0.394	0.383	0.248	2.368

The design event method specifies a rainfall duration of 7 hours for this catchment. The DDF parameters can be used to estimate the 7-hour rainfall for a typical point in the catchment. For example, the 7-hour rainfall with return period 100 years is 66.8 mm.

This is larger than the corresponding estimate in the previous example of 61.4 mm for the 7-hour rainfall at the site of the gauging station, because the Kelvin catchment includes upland areas such as the Campsie Fells, where rainfall estimates are greater.

3.3 The areal reduction factor

The procedure outlined in the previous section provides a design rainfall for a typical *point* in a catchment. Generally, a *catchment-average* design rainfall is required for flood design. Because rainfall is rarely uniform, particularly in extreme storms, the T-year rainfall at a point is bound to be larger than the T-year rainfall over an area. Viewed another way, the atmosphere has to work much harder to exceed a given rainfall depth over a 100 km² catchment than it does to exceed the same depth at one raingauge. The T-year point rainfall must therefore be reduced by an *areal reduction factor* (ARF) to estimate the T-year catchment rainfall. However, no investigation of ARFs was carried out during the FEH research and the ARF results given in the FSR are still used.

3.4 FSR areal reduction factors

The ARF is defined in the FSR as the ratio of the rainfall depth over an area to the rainfall depth of the same duration and return period at a representative point in the area. Areal reduction factors were calculated from a rather obscure analysis of areal and point annual maximum rainfalls in southern England. For each annual maximum areal rainfall, the point rainfalls were noted for each raingauge in the area. The ARF, for a given duration and area, was taken to be the average of the ratios of each point rainfall to the annual maximum point rainfall at the same gauge.

The ARF is assumed to vary only with area and rainfall duration, not with return period or geographical position within the UK. The resulting values of ARF are shown in Figure 3.1. These are the values which are recommended for use in the rainfall-runoff method (Volume 4, §3.2.2).

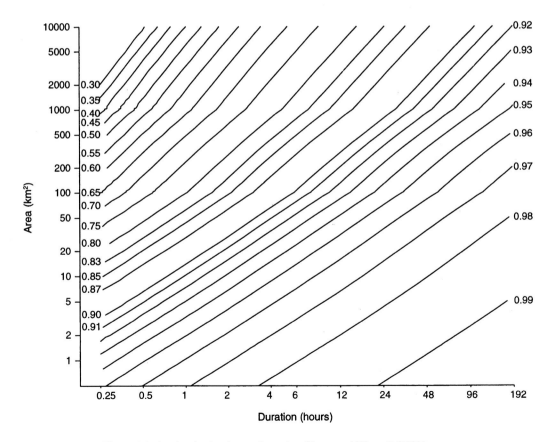

Figure 3.1 *Areal reduction factors based on Keers and Wescott (1977)*

Areal reduction factor formula

The ARFs shown diagrammatically in the FSR have been expressed mathematically by Keers and Wescott (1977). The formula is

$$ARF = 1 - bD^{-a} \tag{3.1}$$

where D is duration in hours and a and b are functions of the area A in km². The values of a and b are given in Table 3.1.

Table 3.1   *Areal reduction factor coefficients (Keers and Wescott, 1977)*

Area A (km²)	a	b
$A \leq 20$	$0.40 - 0.0208 \ln(4.6 - \ln A)$	$0.0394\ A^{0.354}$
$20 < A < 100$	$0.40 - 0.00382\ (4.6 - \ln A)^2$	$0.0394\ A^{0.354}$
$100 \leq A < 500$	$0.40 - 0.00382\ (4.6 - \ln A)^2$	$0.0627\ A^{0.254}$
$500 \leq A < 1000$	$0.40 - 0.0208 \ln(\ln A - 4.6)$	$0.0627\ A^{0.254}$
$1000 \leq A$	$0.40 - 0.0208 \ln(\ln A - 4.6)$	$0.1050\ A^{0.180}$

3.5 Review of FSR ARFs and subsequent research

The ARFs given in the FSR were criticised at the Flood Studies Conference by several delegates. Kelway (1975) and Reynolds (1975) both describe the method of analysis as unsound, as well as pointing out the southerly bias in the data used for the analysis. The method was thought to be unjustified in comparing point rainfalls observed during a particular storm with the highest fall at each gauge in the same year, which is often a totally different event. Kelway preferred the idea of a storm-centred ARF, with a direct physical meaning. The lack of variation in ARF with location or return period was also criticised; Reynolds provided alternative ARFs for north-west Scotland.

A clear explanation of some of the misconceptions underlying these criticisms is provided by Bell (1976), who described the difference between storm-centred and fixed-area ARFs:

- Storm-centred ARFs are calculated for individual rainfall events. The area is usually centred on the most intense part of the storm. Storm-centred ARFs are used mainly for probable maximum precipitation, rather than design rainfalls of a given return period.

- Fixed-area ARFs are not directly related to the ratios of areal to point rainfall in any recorded storm, nor in any hypothetical design storm. Their significance is more statistical than physical. They are simply the ratio between areal and point rainfall of the same return period.

Bell nevertheless pointed out that the FSR method of deriving ARFs is indirect, and depends on assumptions which are not thoroughly tested. He suggested a more direct method, which derives ARFs from the ratio of the point and areal rainfall frequency distributions. This method also has the virtue of indicating any variations of ARF with return period. Based on an analysis of rainfall data from locations across the whole of the UK, Bell's results are generally in good agreement with the FSR. The evidence for any geographic variation in ARFs is inconclusive; the FSR results are found to be slightly overestimated at long return periods.

Similar findings were gained from a study of reservoir safety using raingauge and weather radar data for part of the Pennines in north-west England (Stewart, 1989). Using Bell's method of deriving ARFs, Stewart concluded that ARFs in the study area are slightly smaller than those given in the FSR. They decrease with increasing return period, but vary little with location.

Bell (1976) and Stewart (1989) both concluded that the ARFs given in the FSR err if anything on the side of conservatism, higher ARFs giving larger estimates of areal rainfall. Neither author recommended that the FSR results should be replaced without more definitive research.

Example 3.2

Continuing Example 3.1, the Kelvin at Dryfield has an area of 235 km^2 and a design duration of 7 hours. The corresponding ARF from Equation 3.1 or Figure 3.1 is 0.88.

When this ARF is applied to the 100-year rainfall of 66.8 mm, it yields a catchment rainfall of 59.0 mm.

Special note

Because of a mistake in the digital terrain model for this catchment, it is not possible to reproduce Examples 3.1 and 3.2 using the FEH CD-ROM 1999.

Chapter 4   Choosing a design storm profile

4.1 Requirement

The rainfall-runoff method, described in Volume 4, requires four design variables:

- Rainfall duration;
- Rainfall depth (or return period);
- Storm profile;
- Antecedent catchment wetness.

The storm profile describes the *change in rainfall intensity with time at a point*: it is a temporal rather than a spatial profile. Storm profiles were not investigated in the FEH rainfall frequency research, and the rainfall-runoff method continues to use the profiles given in the Flood Studies Report (FSR). For other flood estimation methods, FEH rainfall statistics may be used with any storm profile, provided that the catchment model is calibrated so that the combination of inputs results in a flood of the required return period. The FSR profiles are also discussed critically in Volume 4, §3.1.1, and their use is described in Volume 4, §3.2.3.

4.2 FSR storm profiles

The storm profiles given in the FSR are symmetric, single-peaked and bell-shaped. Their shape does not vary with storm duration, so that 20-hour storms have the same proportional shape as 2-hour storms. Their shape is also assumed to be invariant with location, although it is recognised that profiles in upland areas tend to be less peaked. The storms analysed for the FSR were split into winter and summer events, centred on the most intense part of the storm, and averaged. There is a range of average profiles, classified by percentage peakedness. The *75% winter profile* is more peaked than 75% of the winter profiles analysed for the FSR.

The two profiles recommended for use in the rainfall-runoff method are the 75% winter profile, for rural catchments, and the 50% summer profile, for urban catchments. The profiles are shown in Figure 4.1 and drawn cumulatively in Figure 4.2, which shows how the proportion of the storm depth varies with

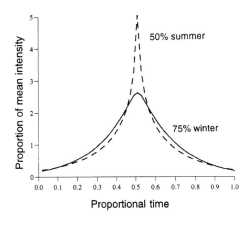

Figure 4.1 Design rainfall profiles, drawn as hyetographs

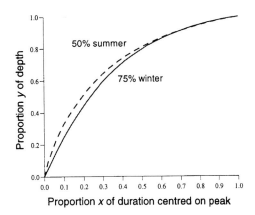

Figure 4.2 Design rainfall profiles, drawn as cumulative proportions of depth, centred on the peak

the proportion of the duration, centred on the peak (a uniform profile would plot as a steadily increasing straight line). The 50% summer profile is more peaked than the 75% winter profile, because of the prevalence of intense convective storms in the summer. These profiles are recommended for durations of "up to several days".

Design storm profile formula

A model for the design profiles was developed for Version 2 of the Micro-FSR software package:

$$y = \frac{1 - a^z}{1 - a} \quad \text{where } z = x^b \tag{4.2}$$

where y is the proportional depth of rain falling in the proportion x of the duration, centred on the peak. The parameters a and b take the following values:

Profile	a	b
75% winter	0.060	1.026
50% summer	0.100	0.815

Note that this formula gives an unrealistically large value for the peak of the 50% summer profile when a very short time step is used.

4.3 Review of FSR profiles and subsequent research

It is easy to criticise the FSR analysis and results for being too simple. The rainfall profiles are based only on information from 24-hour storms, and are obviously unlike most real rainfall events. Criticism started at the Flood Studies Conference: Butters (1975) suggested that the profiles are too peaked for long-duration rainfall and could lead to over-design. Martin (1975) questioned the imposition of symmetry, which neglects the skewness of profiles, particularly important when considering routed floods from reservoirs.

Butters and Vairavamoorthy (1977) sought to use a collection of more realistic rainfall profiles, based more directly on observed rainfall events, for flood design in the Greater London area. Onof *et al.* (1996) assessed this method and compared the use of historical rainfall profiles with randomly generated profiles. Rainfall totals were allocated using the FSR statistics but the design floods were estimated using the FRQSIM model (Vairavamoorthy *et al.*, 1990) rather than the FSR rainfall-runoff method. Onof *et al.* recommended the use of a stochastic rainfall model which can generate 1000 different profiles, from which 1000 flood estimates are produced. Such a technique, which seeks to sample the typical variability in rainfall profiles, is not consistent with the philosophy of a design event method which relies on the use of a single combination of inputs. It is not possible to characterise the variability in all the inputs (as listed in Section 4.1) within the current design event approach to flood estimation.

There are some accepted changes which have been made to the rainfall profiles for use on large reservoired catchments, where the standard FSR profiles are particularly unsuitable. In such catchments, the critical rainfall duration can be as long as ten days, reflecting a sensitivity to a rapid succession of storms which can cause reservoir level to build up over several days. In such cases, it is clearly inappropriate to use a symmetrical storm profile. The Institution of Civil Engineers (1996) recommends the use of the temporal profile of the severest sequence of storms of the required duration that has been observed locally. Johnson *et al.* (1981) put this method into practice in the Highlands of Scotland, using profiles from nine historic storms for flood design.

Stewart and Reynard (1991) used the average variability method (Pilgrim *et al.*, 1969) to derive profiles of 3 to 12-day rainfalls for reservoired catchments in north-west Scotland. The new multi-peaked profiles were compared with those of Johnson *et al.* (1981). A useful review of methods for deriving profiles is given by Reynard and Stewart (1993), who used the average variability method to derive physically realistic profiles for north Wales, north-west Scotland and north-west England. Neither of these more recent papers examined the impact of the profiles on design flood estimation, and there are no specific recommendations for their use in the rainfall-runoff method.

Example

The example at the end of the last chapter derived a 100-year areal rainfall for the Kelvin at Dryfield of 59.0 mm. Because the catchment is less than 25% urbanised, the 75% winter profile is appropriate. The design rainfall duration is 7 hours, and the data interval is 1 hour.

The middle hour is 1/7 of the duration, and the Micro-FSR formula for the 75% winter profile with $x = 0.14$ gives y, the proportion of rain falling in the duration x, equal to 0.34.

The three hours centred on the peak are 3/7 of the duration. Using $x = 0.43$ yields $y = 0.74$. This is the proportion of rain falling in the central three hours. Subtracting 0.34 and dividing by 2 gives the proportion falling in the hour on each side of the peak: 0.20.

Application of the formula to the remaining proportions of the duration yields the following proportional profile:

0.04	0.09	0.20	0.34	0.20	0.09	0.04

which is multiplied by the total rainfall depth to give the design storm profile shown in Figure 4.3.

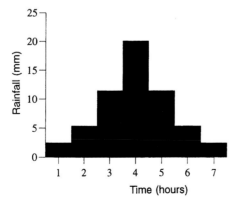

Figure 4.3 *100-year design storm for the Kelvin catchment at Dryfield*

It is important to note that the rainfall-runoff method must be considered as a complete package. There is no guarantee that a rainfall profile of a shape other than the recommended one will produce a design flood of the required return period. For more details, refer to §3.1.1 of FEH Volume 4. Some reassurance for users concerned about the FSR rainfall profiles is provided by Faulkner (1997) who assessed the influence of rainfall duration, depth, profile and antecedent catchment wetness within the rainfall-runoff method. The rainfall profile was found to be of less importance than the other characteristics, for most of the events studied.

The FSR rainfall profiles continue to be used in the Wallingford Procedure for urban drainage analysis and design (DOE, 1981), which is incorporated in software packages such as HydroWorks. The procedure incorporates a filter which smooths the point profile for use over a catchment. Later modifications of the procedure include an alternative option to use a typical annual rainfall time-series which is more appropriate than a single design storm for estimating the frequency and volume of discharges from combined sewer overflows (Garside, 1991).

Chapter 5   Worked examples of rainfall frequency calculations

5.1 Introduction

These examples illustrate the use of the rainfall frequency software. They are not intended to show all the stages involved in the underlying analysis, only the work done by the FEH software. There are more examples of return period assessments in Chapter 15.

5.2 What is the 2-day rainfall with return period 100 years for Norwich?

The user wants the rainfall at a point (the centre of Norwich) over a duration of two measurement days, with return period 100 years.

The grid reference of Norwich in metres is (622000 308000). At this point, the 1-km gridded DDF parameters stored on the CD-ROM are:

c	d_1	d_2	d_3	e	f
−0.023	0.273	0.351	0.236	0.309	2.488

When the DDF model is supplied with these parameters, a duration of 48 hours and a return period of 100 years, it produces a design rainfall of 106 mm (Figure 5.1).

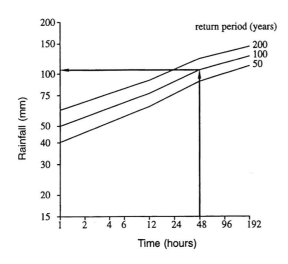

Figure 5.1 DDF plot for Norwich

This rainfall total must be adjusted to account for discretisation. A rainfall aggregated over a sliding duration of 48 hours should be divided by 1.11 to estimate a rainfall aggregated over a fixed duration of 2 days (Table 2.1). Thus the 2-day 100-year rainfall for Norwich is 95 mm.

5.3 What is the 4-hour rainfall with return period 20 years for a typical point in the Lyne catchment?

The River Lyne drains the Bewcastle Fells in northern Cumbria. It is prone to flash flooding, particularly since the digging of drainage ditches during the afforestation of the upper parts of the catchment. The catchment area at the A7 road bridge at Westlinton is 228 km².

The subject site location software can be used in conjunction with a map to find the grid reference of the River Lyne at the A7 bridge to the nearest 50 m: (339350 564700). At this point, the catchment-average DDF parameters stored on the CD-ROM are:

c	d_1	d_2	d_3	e	f
−0.025	0.344	0.485	0.402	0.287	2.374

When the DDF model is supplied with these parameters, a duration of 4 hours and a return period of 20 years, it produces a design rainfall of 36.5 mm (Figure 5.2). This is a typical point rainfall for the Lyne catchment. The figure could be adjusted to an areal rainfall by multiplying by the ARF, and then used in a rainfall-runoff calculation.

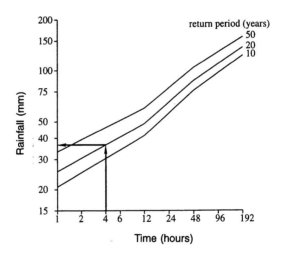

Figure 5.2 DDF plot for Lyne catchment at A7 road bridge

5.4 How rare was the rainfall of 6th August 1978 at Broughshane, County Antrim?

Assessing the rarity of a storm can be rather subjective. Aside from the question of defining the start and end of the storm, there are many aspects of rainfall events, such as the total rainfall in different places, the duration, the extent, the impact and the spatial and temporal profiles. A storm may be rare in terms of any of these characteristics. It is usual to estimate the return period of the largest rainfall total. Unless the event lasts for several days, data from a recording raingauge (or suitably calibrated weather radar) are required for an accurate assessment. Daily totals may be helpful in cases where there was no rainfall in the day apart from the storm, if observers can say how long the event lasted.

Recording raingauge data are available from Broughshane from 6 August 1978, when an occluded front moved over Northern Ireland, bringing cool weather and heavy thundery showers. 47.7 mm fell in 5 hours, from 1:00 am.

The Irish grid reference of the gauge is (316400 408900), at which point the DDF parameters are:

c	d_1	d_2	d_3	e	f
−0.022	0.412	0.551	0.276	0.261	2.252

These values lead to an estimated return period of 68 years. The largest hourly total within the event was 28.6 mm, which has a return period of 69 years.

If there had been no hourly data and no accounts of the duration of the event, the total from a daily gauge on site would have given the only approximation to the rarity of the event. The daily total, from a gauge read at 9 am, was also 47.7 mm. This must be converted into an equivalent depth for a sliding duration before being supplied to the DDF model. The adjustment involves multiplying by 1.16 (Table 2.1), to give 55.3 mm. The estimated return period of this depth in 24 hours is only 7 years. Thus the daily total gives a poor estimate of the return period of the 5-hour storm.

C Supporting theory and results

Chapter 6   Introduction to the analysis

6.1 Annual maximum approach to rainfall frequency analysis

Frequency analysis can be based either on annual maximum (AM) data or peak-over-threshold (POT) data. The AM series comprises the largest rainfall observed in each year, whereas POT data consist of the time and magnitude of rainfalls exceeding a threshold. POT data provide more information than AM data because there is generally more than one value per year, which is an advantage for exploiting short records. However, regional analysis and in particular the study of spatial dependence is much more difficult for POT data. Another reason for preferring AM data is the availability of plentiful annual maximum data for sub-daily rainfall durations for sites where POT data have not been abstracted from the chart records (Chapter 13). A more comprehensive comparison of the relative merits of AM and POT approaches for analysing rainfall data is given by Stewart *et al.* (1999).

The FEH rainfall frequency analysis uses the annual maximum depths of rainfall for calendar years aggregated over various durations from 1 hour to 8 days. The two key parts to the analysis are the mapping of an index variable, and the derivation of growth curves.

6.2 The index variable, RMED

The index variable was chosen to be the median of annual maximum rainfalls at a site, RMED. The median is used in preference to the mean as it is a more robust statistic which is unaffected by the presence of unusually large or small values in the annual maximum series. In addition, the median value corresponds to a defined return period of two years on the annual maximum scale. RMED is evaluated for eight key durations, from 1 hour to 8 days. See Chapter 7 for a description of the mapping of RMED and some of the results.

6.3 Growth curve estimation with FORGEX

The other key component of the analysis is the derivation of rainfall growth curves. Growth curves enable the estimation of the T-year extreme rainfall relative to an index extreme rainfall, in this case RMED. Series of annual maximum rainfalls are standardised by dividing by RMED. Rainfall growth curves, for various durations, are derived by the FORGEX method, which was developed specifically for the FEH. The acronym FORGEX stands for FOcused Rainfall Growth curve EXtension. The method is outlined in Chapter 8, and Chapter 9 describes the derivation of confidence limits for growth curves.

6.4 The DDF model and discussion of the results

During the mapping of RMED and the derivation of growth curves, each rainfall duration was treated separately. The results were then incorporated into a model linking rainfall depth, duration and frequency (a DDF model), as explained in Chapter 10. Chapter 11 presents and discusses example maps of rainfall growth rates and design rainfall for the UK. Chapter 12 contains guidance on using the results for very long or short durations, advice on incorporating additional local data, and a discussion of fluctuations, trends and climate change.

Chapter 7 Estimating and mapping the index rainfall

7.1 Estimating RMED

The index variable, RMED, is defined as the median of annual maximum rainfalls (for a given duration) at a site. Values of RMED for eight rainfall durations between 1 hour and 8 days were estimated from series of annual maximum rainfall throughout the UK.

A required minimum record length of nine years ensures that RMED is reasonably estimated. The estimates will still be susceptible to climatic fluctuations, but the chosen minimum record length is a compromise between having too short and too few records. There are many new sub-daily rainfall records around ten years long, some of which are in remote areas and are thus particularly valuable in the mapping of RMED.

Digital maps of RMED on a 1-km grid were required for eventual combination with rainfall growth rates. The mapping involved interpolation between the sites of raingauges where the sample values of RMED are known. The interpolation made use of topographic information from a digital terrain model (DTM). A more detailed account of the mapping is given in a paper by Faulkner and Prudhomme (1998). Note that catchment-average values of RMED are also supplied with the FEH for use as catchment descriptors (Volume 5) but these should not to be used in rainfall frequency estimation.

7.2 Mapping RMED by georegression

7.2.1 Introduction to georegression

Georegression is an extension of the interpolation method known as *kriging*, which is based on the theory of geostatistics (Journel and Huijbregts, 1978).

Stewart *et al.* (1995) found that kriging is a good method for mapping RMED in the Severn catchment. Ordinary kriging works well in lowland Britain, where there is a dense network of daily raingauges providing sample values of RMED (Figure 13.1). However, RMED is less well sampled in mountainous areas. In addition, the network of recording raingauges (which provide values of RMED for durations 1 to 24 hours) is much sparser in all areas, as can be seen from Figure 13.3. One avenue for improving the interpolation is to incorporate information from covariates (secondary variables) which are related to rainfall. Covariates such as elevation, distance from the coast or more subtle topographic

---

Kriging

Geostatistics involves analysing the spatial structure of a variable by deriving a semivariogram, which describes how the variance between pairs of points changes with their separation. A model is fitted to the experimental semivariogram, and this model is then used in the *ordinary kriging* process which assigns values to ungauged locations using a weighted linear combination of nearby sample values. Kriging also produces a measure of uncertainty, the kriging variance, at any location.

D. S. Faulkner & C. Prudhomme **21**

variables can be derived from a DTM and evaluated at every 1-km grid node (Prudhomme and Reed, 1998).

One way to incorporate covariates is via the method of *cokriging*. This involves the estimation of cross-variograms which describe the spatial relationships between the variable of interest and prospective covariates, for example the relationship between rainfall and altitude at pairs of sites. Stewart *et al.* (1995) tried cokriging for mapping RMED, using altitude as the covariate. They found that cokriging offers no improvement over ordinary kriging, possibly because of the poor correlation between RMED and altitude in the Severn catchment.

Cokriging becomes difficult to apply when there is more than one covariate. *Georegression* is a simpler alternative which makes use of any number of covariates. A regression model relating the primary variable with the covariates is used to estimate the primary variable at all sites. The estimates are improved by combining them with residuals, which are interpolated (by ordinary kriging) between gauge locations. The technique has also been termed elevation-detrended kriging (Phillips *et al.*, 1992) and modified residual kriging (Prudhomme and Reed, 1998).

Georegression

The georegression procedure has the following steps:

(i) Relationships between RMED and topography are investigated, and a regression model is fitted.

(ii) Differences between the observed and the estimated RMED (i.e. the residuals) are calculated at all raingauge sites.

(iii) The residuals are interpolated, using ordinary kriging, to give a map of correction factors to apply to the regression estimates.

(iv) The map of regression estimates is combined with the map of correction factors to give the final map of RMED.

7.2.2 Topographic variables

The most familiar topographic effect on rainfall is that it increases with altitude. This simple orographic effect is moderated by a secondary phenomenon, the rainshadow effect and, in large upland areas such as the Cairngorm mountains, by rain-out of the low level moisture before it reaches the highest summits. In fact the relationship between precipitation and topography is complex, and factors such as the slope, exposure, distance to a barrier and distance from the moisture source can all be important (Konrad, 1996).

The regression analysis made use of a large number of topographic variables which were designed to represent some of the more subtle effects of topography on rainfall. The variables are described in detail by Prudhomme and Reed (1998), who developed them for a study of the Highlands of Scotland, and only those found to be significant in the regression models are described here. The variables are derived from a 1-km DTM, and calculated for eight cardinal directions (N, NE, E, SE, S, SW, W, NW) and, for some variables, in two additional directions (WSW, ENE). These variables were initially evaluated at the DTM grid points closest to each raingauge. When the maps of RMED were produced, the variables were calculated for every grid point.

Average elevation is an alternative to a simple point elevation suggested by Konrad (1996). ELEV10 is the arithmetic mean elevation in metres of the typically 121 DTM grid-points in a 10 × 10 km square centred on the location.

Continentality is an effect which seeks to represent the greater frequency of thunderstorms in south-east England. It is indexed by DLILLE, the distance in km from Lille in the north of France.

The remaining topographic variables are all calculated and averaged over a 90° sector centred on the main direction of interest **d**, where **d** is N, NE, E, etc. This helps to overcome the weakness of variables that are defined by topographic properties along a single straight line. The value of such variables is dependent on the DTM-grid points found in one direction only, which may represent a small feature such as a hill or a narrow sea loch which has little influence on the precipitation at the point.

Figure 7.1 illustrates the definition of the following three variables. The plan view shows the 90° sector centred on the direction **d** and one of eleven secondary directions radiating at angle α from the location of interest. The variables are averaged over these eleven directions, each value being weighted by cos a to give more weight to directions close to **d**. The longitudinal section shows the gauge and the horizon in one direction.

Distance from sea (SEA) is the weighted average of the 11 distances (in km) from the sea centred on the direction of interest **d**.

Obstruction (OBST) represents the average angle subtended by the highest topographic barrier in a sector centred on **d**. It is defined as the weighted average of the eleven tangents of the angles subtended by the horizon, ($\Delta h/\Delta x$), with units m km^{-1}. The smallest value OBST can take is zero, for a totally exposed site.

Barrier (BAR) is the weighted average of the eleven distances (in km) to the horizon, Δx. Unfortunately this variable cannot be defined at totally exposed sites, such as some points on the coast. Due to this difficulty, and a tendency for sudden jumps in the variable at the tops of ridges, the variable was eventually excluded from the regression analysis.

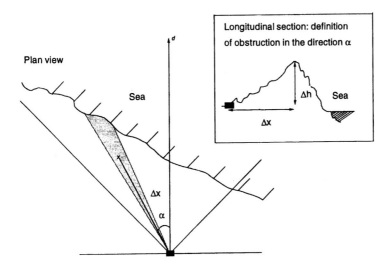

Figure 7.1 *Distances used in the definition of the variables SEA, OBST and BAR*

Other variables included in the regression analysis included point elevation, geographical position, slope, roughness of the terrain, and lightning strike density. None of these was included in the final regression models.

7.2.3 The regression model for long-duration RMED: 1 to 8 days

Single-variable regressions between RMED and the various topographic variables were used to explore the relationships between RMED and topography. For each rainfall duration, a model for RMED was then built using multiple regression analysis. The maximum number of explanatory variables to be included in each model was limited to four.

In addition to the proportion of variance explained by the model, the following criteria were considered when selecting variables for inclusion in the model. Explanatory variables should not be highly correlated with each other and, where possible, models should respect physical explanations for variations in rainfall. For example, considering that most long-duration rainfall extremes in the UK are associated with the prevailing westerly and south-westerly winds, explanatory variables oriented W-E or SW-NE are more likely to be physically meaningful in modelling long-duration RMED than those oriented N-S or NW-SE.

For long-duration RMED the regression analysis was focused on the mountainous regions of the UK. Topography and relief are expected to be more clearly correlated here there than in regions with less varied relief. The priority in model-building was to fit the data well in these sparsely-gauged mountain regions. Elsewhere, it was expected that the good density of sample values (Figure 13.1) would enable the interpolated residuals to account for any variations in the fit of the model. After several alternative groups of gauges were tried, the model was fitted to data from the 1589 raingauges in a "Celtic" region comprising the Scottish Highlands, north-west England, Wales (minus the Severn catchment) and south-west England. A separate regression model was fitted in Northern Ireland.

Least-squares regression relies on an assumption of constant variance, i.e. no relationship between the squared residuals and the predicted variable. Several transformations of the primary variable, RMED, were tried in order to increase compliance with the assumption. The final model was framed in terms of the most effective transformed variable, which was 1000/RMED. The multiplier 1000 was introduced to avoid numerical problems in the kriging process.

The model-building technique was a stepwise multiple regression: variables were added to the model one at a time. The preferred model for 1000/(1-day RMED) is:

$$1000/RMED = 26.39 - 0.070 \, OBST_w - 0.028 \, ELEV10 + 0.053 \, SEA_{wsw} \qquad (7.1)$$

where RMED is in mm. This model explains 53% of the variance of the transformed variable in the Celtic region and 57% of the variance in the whole of Great Britain. The model makes physical sense: the rainfall increases with average elevation and with the obstruction to the west, which reflects orographic enhancement of rainfall moving from the west. RMED decreases with distance from the sea in the west-southwest direction, in accordance with the prevailing wind direction.

For rainfall durations longer than one day, models were fitted to the same triplet of topographic variables, since broadly similar processes govern extreme rainfall for durations between 1 and 8 days. The coefficients of the equations for 1, 2, 4 and 8-day rainfall are given in Table 7.1. The coefficients vary smoothly with rainfall duration. For longer durations, somewhat more of the variance is explained by the model. The topographic effects represented by the model have more influence on longer-duration rainfall extremes.

Regional versions of the regression models were considered, in order to avoid mixing so much data from climatically different areas. However, they would introduce difficult problems at region boundaries. A separate model for Northern Ireland was possible, though, where records are available from 269 raingauges with at least ten annual maxima, including 27 in border areas of the Republic of Ireland. The coefficients of the models for Northern Ireland are given in Table 7.2.

Table 7.1 *Coefficients of regression models for 1000/RMED for long durations in Great Britain*

Duration (days)	Constant	$OBST_{sw}$	ELEV10	SEA_{wsw}	r^2 (%)
1	26.39	-0.070	-0.028	0.053	53
2	20.22	-0.063	-0.023	0.041	58
4	14.86	-0.050	-0.019	0.038	61
8	10.35	-0.038	-0.014	0.032	62

Table 7.2 *Coefficients of regression models for 1000/RMED for long durations in Northern Ireland*

Duration (days)	Constant	$OBST_{sw}$	ELEV10	SEA_{sw}	SEA_{E}	r^2 (%)
1	19.08	-0.097	-0.048	0.056	0.047	64
2	16.26	-0.084	-0.037	0.036	0.033	67
4	14.46	-0.073	-0.033	0.024	0.015	71
8	11.08	-0.054	-0.023	0.017	0.004	68

7.2.4 The regression models for short-duration RMED: 1 to 12 hours

Maps of short-duration RMED were produced at four key durations: 1, 2, 6 and 12 hours. Short-duration rainfall extremes are more difficult to model, mainly because of a lack of data (Figure 13.3 indicates the sparsity of recording raingauges in some areas). The difficulty is greatest at the shortest rainfall duration, 1 hour, since short-duration rainfalls tend to be affected least by topography (Institute of Engineers, Australia, 1987). Additionally, there are large variations in the sample values of 1-hour RMED over short distances, particularly in eastern England.

It was thought that data connected with thunderstorm activity might help explain these variations, and so lightning strike data were included in the analysis. Unfortunately they explained little of the variance in RMED. The relationship between lightning strike rate and extreme rainfall is not simple. In a convective storm lightning strikes do not necessarily occur at the same time as heavy rainfall, and therefore, if the storm is moving, may occur in a different location. Also, over time, locations prone to lightning strikes are not necessarily prone to heavy rainfall. An additional covariate used for modelling short-duration RMED was the final interpolated 1-day RMED (RMEDDY) at the site of the recording raingauge. This represents a combination of topographic variables (listed in the previous two tables) and daily rainfall data, and has an increasing influence on short-duration RMED as the duration increases. Over 70% of the variation in 12-hour RMED is explained by the interpolated 1-day RMED.

The number of sites offering sub-daily data for Northern Ireland is not sufficient to fit a separate regression model, so data from the whole of the UK are considered simultaneously.

For short durations, RMED was not transformed, as transformations did not improve the basis of the regression. A multiple regression analysis, guided by the choice of physically realistic variables, selected three explanatory variables, $OBST_{NW}$ (obstruction to the northwest), DLILLE (index of continentality) and RMEDDY (interpolated 1-day RMED). The coefficients of $OBST_{NW}$ and DLILLE, were found to vary only slightly with duration. A single coefficient was therefore adopted for each variable, and the difference between durations is accounted for by a change in the constant and, most significantly, in the coefficient of RMEDDY. A final regression, combining all four durations, produced the models for short-duration RMED specified in Table 7.3. The value of r^2 increases dramatically with duration, from 29% for 1-hour rainfall to 69% for 12-hour rainfall, partly because of the increasing relevance of RMEDDY for longer durations.

The presence of the topographic variable $OBST_{NW}$ supports a finding of May and Hitch (1989b). They mapped 1-hour rainfall with a return period of 5 years in the UK and looked at the results along a swath running approximately southeast-northwest through London and into the English Midlands. The largest 1–hour rainfall totals appear to be co-located with south-east facing ground slopes. May and Hitch suggested that this was an effect of heavy rainfall produced by orographic uplifting associated with summer thunderstorms which develop over France, cross the English channel and travel into the English Midlands. The models for RMED in Table 7.3, with a negative coefficient for $OBST_{NW}$, support this interpretation, producing larger values for extreme rainfall on south-east facing slopes.

Table 7.3 *Coefficients of regression models for short-duration RMED in the UK*

Duration (hours)	Constant	$OBST_{NW}$	DLILLE	RMEDDY	r^2 (%)
1	9.29	-0.032	-0.0035	0.909	29
2	10.20	-0.032	-0.0035	0.189	32
6	8.45	-0.032	-0.0035	0.516	63
12	7.31	-0.032	-0.0035	0.744	69

7.2.5 Interpolating the residuals

The models specified in Tables 7.1 to 7.3 were used to estimate 1000/RMED for long durations and RMED for short durations at every point across the UK. Residuals were calculated at the sites of raingauges and interpolated on to a 1 km grid using ordinary kriging. A slight local smoothing was added, to ensure that information from surrounding gauges was always used, even if a sample coincided exactly with a grid point. This simply involved imposing a minimum distance of 500 m between the grid point and a sample.

The residuals account for geographic variations in RMED not represented by the regression models. For example, the residuals of 1-day RMED are large over the Grampian mountains in Scotland, where the regression model does not account for the rainshadow effect, by which rainfall over the Grampians is smaller than in areas of similar elevation further west in Scotland.

7.3 *Estimating the uncertainty of RMED*

The uncertainty in the final estimates of RMED is due to uncertainty in the regression (measured by the standard error) and in the kriging. Uncertainty in kriging is measured by the *kriging variance*, which is produced by the kriging algorithm for every grid point.

Kriging variance

The kriging variance is due both to the layout of the samples and the semivariogram model used. When, as in this study, isotropic semivariogram models are used, the kriging variance is affected only by the density of samples around the grid point (and not their directions). The kriging variance is high in sparsely gauged areas.

The kriging variance is that of the residuals. For 1-day RMED, the final estimate of RMED is given by reversing the transformation specified in §7.2.3, thus:

$$\text{RMED}_{\text{final}} = \frac{1000}{(1000 \; / \; \text{RMED}_{\text{modelled}}) - \text{residual}} \qquad (7.2)$$

where $\text{RMED}_{\text{modelled}}$ is the estimate from the regression model (Equation 7.1). The variance of $\text{RMED}_{\text{final}}$ can be estimated using the formula for the variance of a function F of x and y:

$$\text{var}\,[F(x,y)] = \left(\frac{\partial F(0)}{\partial x}\right)^2 \text{var}\,[x] + \left(\frac{\partial F(0)}{\partial y}\right)^2 \text{var}\,[y] \qquad (7.3)$$

provided that x and y are independent. Unfortunately this is far from true in this case, where x represents $\text{RMED}_{\text{modelled}}$ and y the residual. The variance of $\text{RMED}_{\text{modelled}}$ is less than the squared standard error of the regression because the residuals are being accounted for. As a first approximation, the uncertainty of the regression is ignored and the overall variance is estimated from the kriging variance alone. Differentiating Equation 7.2 with respect to the residual, and taking the square root to find the standard deviation σ yields:

$$\sigma\,[\,\text{RMED}_{\text{final}}\,] \approx \frac{\text{RMED}_{\text{modelled}}{}^2}{1000}\;\sigma\,[\text{residual}] \qquad (7.4)$$

where $\sigma[\text{residual}]$ is the square root of the kriging variance.

For 1-hour RMED, which is not transformed in the regression model, the standard deviation is approximated simply by the square root of the kriging variance. Maps of the standard deviation are discussed in the following section.

7.4 *Maps of 1-day and 1-hour RMED and standard deviation*

Figure 7.2 is a map of median annual maximum 1-day rainfall (RMED) over the UK, a combination of the regression model results and the map of residuals. The maps for 2 to 8-day RMED have a similar pattern. The largest values of RMED are

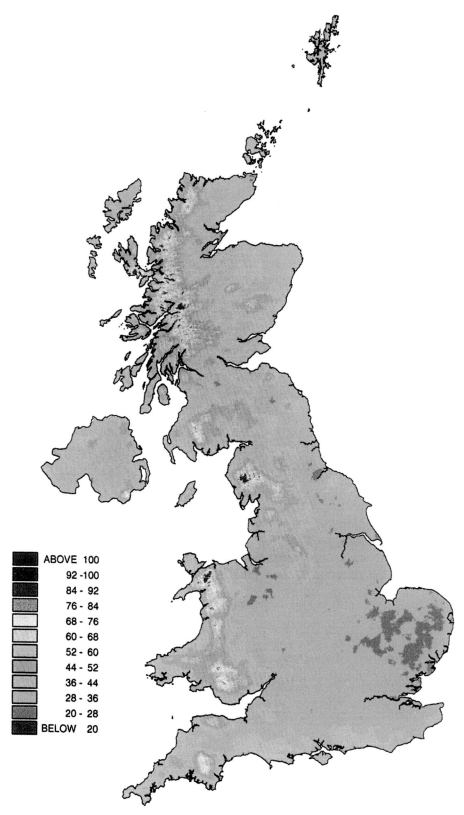

| ABOVE 100 |
| 92 -100 |
| 84 - 92 |
| 76 - 84 |
| 68 - 76 |
| 60 - 68 |
| 52 - 60 |
| 44 - 52 |
| 36 - 44 |
| 28 - 36 |
| 20 - 28 |
| BELOW 20 |

Figure 7.2 *1-day RMED (mm)*

found in mountainous regions, and especially in the western parts of the mountains. The south coast is generally wetter than more inland areas, and the smallest values can be found at the east coast, especially in East Anglia.

Figure 7.3 is a map of 1-hour RMED. The largest values are again in the western uplands, but there are also areas in eastern and southern England with increased RMED, thought to reflect convective storm activity. The smallest values are in eastern Scotland. There is no particular sign that RMED is higher in urban areas, despite evidence that urban heat island effects influence the initiation and development of convective storms (Thielen and Gadian, 1997). Note that the grids of RMED extend slightly further than is shown on the figures, into parts of the Republic of Ireland which drain into Northern Ireland. This is to permit the calculation of catchment-average figures for rivers such as the Erne which extend into the Republic of Ireland.

Figures 7.4 and 7.5 are maps of the standard deviation of 1-day and 1-hour RMED, approximated as described in Section 7.3.

The standard deviation of 1-day RMED is given by Equation 7.4, in which $RMED_{modelled}$ is raised to the power of two. This means that Figure 7.4 is strongly influenced by the magnitude of RMED, and the highest uncertainty is in the wettest areas (compare with Figure 7.2). The 1000/RMED transformation which was required for the regression thus introduces extra uncertainty to the results, particularly in areas of high RMED. The influence of the kriging variance can be seen in the high uncertainty over the Grampian mountains, where the density of gauges is small (Figure 13.1). Over much of lowland Britain, the standard deviation is small, between 1 and 2.5 mm.

The standard deviation of 1-hour RMED (Figure 7.5) is approximated by the kriging error alone, and thus has a much narrower range of values across the country. It is directly related to the density of raingauges with available data (Section 7.3). Figure 7.5 reveals striking differences in the density of recording raingauges across the UK. The best gauged area is Greater London, followed by the English Midlands. The west of Scotland is particularly poorly gauged. For England and Wales, there are gaps in the gauge network in south-west England and north Wales. Maps such as this could provide useful information to guide the siting of additional recording raingauges, or the digitising of existing charts from tilting syphon gauges.

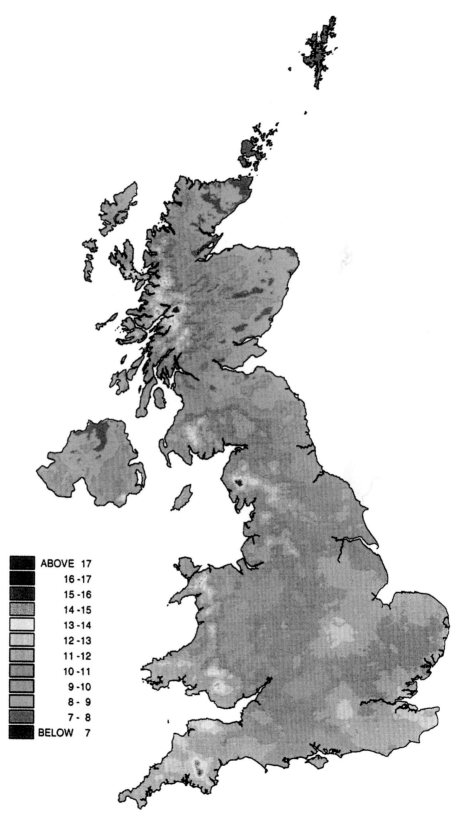

Figure 7.3 *1-hour RMED (mm)*

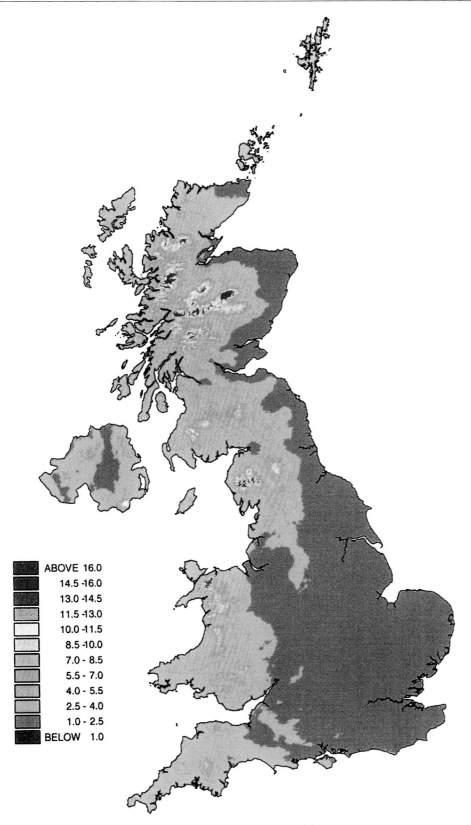

Figure 7.4 *Standard deviation of 1-day RMED (in mm) due to kriging*

Legend:
ABOVE 16.0
14.5 -16.0
13.0 -14.5
11.5 -13.0
10.0 -11.5
8.5 -10.0
7.0 - 8.5
5.5 - 7.0
4.0 - 5.5
2.5 - 4.0
1.0 - 2.5
BELOW 1.0

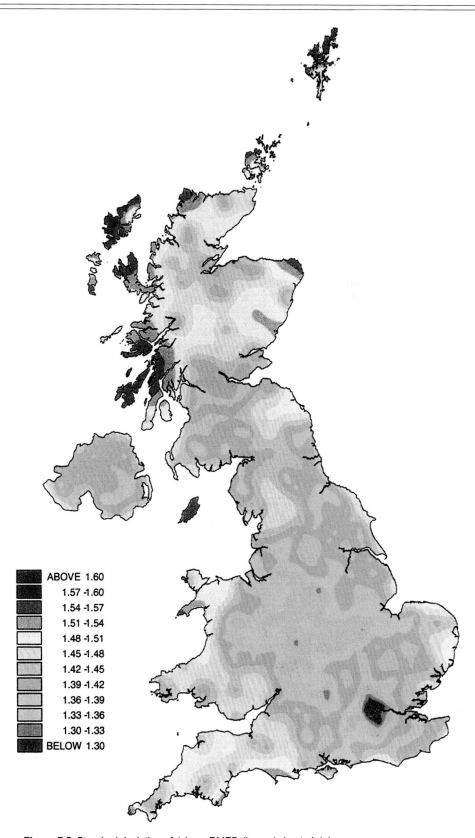

ABOVE 1.60
1.57 -1.60
1.54 -1.57
1.51 -1.54
1.48 -1.51
1.45 -1.48
1.42 -1.45
1.39 -1.42
1.36 -1.39
1.33 -1.36
1.30 -1.33
BELOW 1.30

Figure 7.5 Standard deviation of 1-hour RMED (in mm) due to kriging

Chapter 8   Deriving growth curves

8.1 Introduction and context

Rainfall growth curves are derived by the FORGEX method. FORGEX is capable of estimating rare extreme rainfalls, with return periods of up to 2000 years, and is a rather complicated method. Its key features are explained here but for a fuller description refer to the paper by Reed *et al.* (1999).

FORGEX is a development of the FORGE method (Reed and Stewart, 1989) which was designed to overcome some of the problems in the FSR rainfall growth factors. The FSR results have been described as over-general, masking important local and regional variations in rainfall frequency. Bootman and Willis (1977) expressed concern about the applicability of the FSR growth factors to Somerset and the surrounding region, demonstrating that the method seriously underestimates the magnitude of 2-day rainfalls. This was supported by Clark (1997) and Dales and Reed (1989), who also found that the FSR tends to underestimate rainfall in eastern England and overestimate in north-west England. Kelway (1975) and Reed and Stewart (1989) criticised the FSR method for failing to account for spatial dependence in rainfall extremes. Stewart *et al.* (1999) present a review of rainfall frequency estimation in the UK.

FORGEX is based on the analysis of annual maximum rainfalls. Its key features are:

- the median of at-site annual maxima, RMED, is used as the index variable;
- individual durations are treated separately in the construction of growth curves;
- growth curves are focused on the site of interest, rather than applying to rigid regions;
- annual maxima are pooled from a network of gauges which expands with return period, giving precedence to the use of local data;
- shifted network maximum rainfalls account for inter-site dependence in rainfall extremes;
- the growth curve is seamlessly extended to long return periods;
- the growth curve is made up of linear segments on a Gumbel scale, avoiding an explicit distributional assumption.

FORGEX is a empirical, graphical method in that it plots points on a rainfall-return period scale and then fits a line through the points. It represents a departure from approaches which fit assumed distributions using methods such as L-moments or maximum likelihood.

8.2 Focusing, pooling and homogeneity

The simplest growth curves are derived from data at one site only. To obtain growth rates for longer return periods with more confidence, it is necessary to use data from several sites in a region. A disadvantage of fixed regions is that sharp discontinuities in growth rates at regional boundaries are difficult to avoid. For example, there is a discontinuity in the FSR growth rates at the Scotland - England border, which is the boundary between the two regions used for the FSR analysis. For a discussion of several methods of regional rainfall frequency estimation, refer to Buishand (1991).

<blockquote>

Pooling

Regional frequency analysis involves combining data from several sites in a region. This is referred to as pooling. In a graphical method such as FORGEX, each series of annual maximum values is plotted on a Gumbel reduced variate scale, so that data from different sites are superposed. It should not be confused with the station-year method, in which series from a group of sites are concatenated to form one long series.

</blockquote>

The FORGEX method pools data from circular regions centred on the subject site, or *focal point*. Because the regions for each site are slightly different, the resulting growth rates vary smoothly across the country. Rather than using one region centred on each site, FORGEX pools data from a hierarchy of raingauge networks. One of the principles driving the development of FORGEX was the use of local data wherever possible. Data from smaller networks are used to estimate the growth curve for short return periods. For longer return periods, local data do not adequately define the growth curve (because there are insufficient series, and there is unlikely to be a long one) and so data from larger networks are drawn in to the analysis. The size of a region is therefore a compromise between keeping the region small (and therefore relevant) and avoiding excessive extrapolation.

As successive networks are constructed, the radius of the circle is increased and annual maximum rainfalls are drawn together from larger numbers of sites. The name of the method is taken from this idea of focusing the analysis on the site for which the growth curve is required. The rules which govern the expansion of the gauge network are given by Reed *et al.* (1999).

An upper limit of 200 km (for the UK) is set for the network radius. This guards against the pooling of data from sites of radically different climate, while allowing the method to gain access to enough observations to support the definition of the growth curve at long return periods. Figure 8.1 shows the networks used for deriving a 1-day growth curve focused on Leicester.

<blockquote>

Homogeneity

In regional frequency analysis it is assumed that data are pooled from a *homogeneous* region, i.e. the data are all drawn from the same frequency distribution. Sites which do not fit well within a region are termed *discordant*.

</blockquote>

The regions used for FORGEX are defined only by distance from the focal point. For a variable such as rainfall (as opposed to flood peaks) a statistic such as geographical location is a good indication of similarity between frequency distributions, and thus useful for defining regions. The development of the method included some tests for heterogeneity and discordancy, based on L-moment statistics (Hosking and Wallis, 1997). When L-moment statistics appear to show that a site is discordant, Hosking and Wallis recommend that the site should be retained in the region if the discordancy can be explained by random meteorological events that could equally well occur at other sites. In the words of Bilham (1935), "One thing is very clear, namely that the incidence of heavy rains in short periods is very fortuitous". Most discordant sites in FORGEX regions are probably due to such effects.

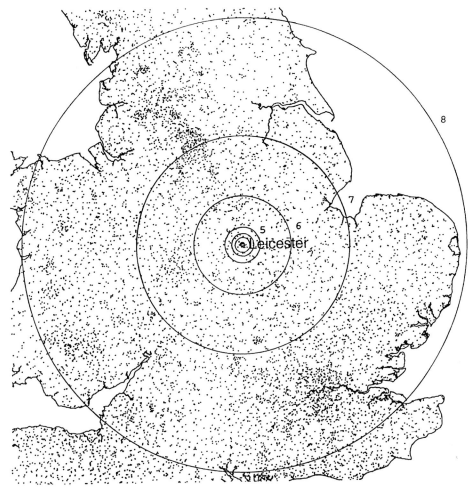

Figure 8.1 Networks of daily raingauges focused on Leicester

The FORGEX method thus assesses homogeneity on the basis of distance alone. A variant could be developed to respect particular climatic features. For example, networks might be defined by ellipses to encourage pooling along coasts. Other schemes might be devised to pool data from sites which share a characteristic exposure to, or shelter from, typical rain-producing weather systems.

8.3 Plotting positions

Annual maxima from individual records, with a minimum length of 10 years, are ranked and allocated plotting positions on a Gumbel reduced variate scale. Following established practice (Shaw, 1994), the Gringorten plotting position formula is used:

$$F(i) = (i - 0.44) / (N + 0.12) \qquad (8.1)$$

where $F(i)$ is the non-exceedance probability, i the rank in increasing order, and N the number of annual maxima. The Gumbel reduced variate is defined by:

$$y = -\ln(-\ln F) \qquad (8.2)$$

Not all points are plotted (see the next section), and only points which are plotted are used to fit the growth curve.

8.4 Definition of y-slices

Each raingauge network in the hierarchy is associated with the definition of the growth curve within a particular *y-slice*. The *y*-slices have width 1.0 on the Gumbel reduced variate scale, and the first one ends at $y = 0.3665$ which is the position of the median (T = 2 years). Pooled data points which are plotted within the *j*th *y*-slice come from gauges within the *j*th network. This ensures that local data are used in preference to data from further afield.

Larger networks include more long-record stations, and thus provide pooled data points that plot in *y*-slices that correspond to rarer events. However, there are few sites in the UK with records longer than about 100 years. This means that pooled points alone cannot define the growth curve beyond about the fifth *y*-slice. Figure 8.2 shows the points plotted from networks focused on Leicester. Pooled annual maximum 1-day rainfalls are shown as dots. There are only two pooled points plotted at a return period longer than 200 years. The plotted numbers are explained in the next section.

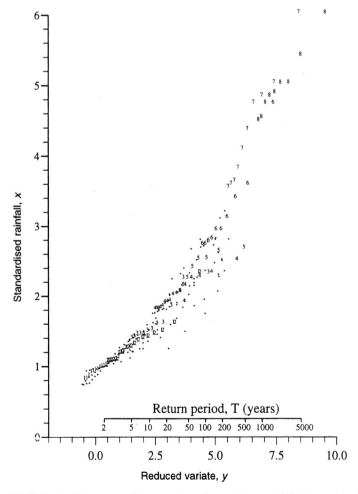

Figure 8.2 *Plotted points representing annual maximum 1-day rainfalls focused on Leicester*

8.5 Network maximum points

The *network maximum* (netmax) series is defined as the annual maximum series of the largest standardised value recorded by the network of raingauges. There is one netmax value for each year of record.

Dales and Reed (1989) show that the distribution of the network maximum from N independent and identically distributed General Extreme Value (GEV) distributions lies exactly ln N to the left of the regional growth curve on a Gumbel reduced variate scale, and Reed and Stewart (1994) note that this result is not restricted to the GEV. In practice, because of inter-site dependence in annual maxima, the netmax growth curve is found to lie a shorter distance to the left. Dales and Reed label this distance $\ln N_e$, terming N_e the effective number of independent gauges.

Thus, spatial dependence can be assessed from the relationship between typical and network maximum growth curves. Conversely, the fitting of the regional growth curve can be aided by information on spatial dependence. If an estimate of N_e is available, the top part of the netmax series can provide valuable information to guide the extension of the regional growth curve to long return periods. N_e could of course simply be estimated from the separation between the typical and netmax growth curves, but a more reliable estimate would combine results from many growth curve analyses.

Spatial dependence and the station-year method

Because rainstorms can affect large areas, annual maximum rainfalls recorded at different gauges in the same year may be due to the same storm. These annual maxima are said to exhibit *spatial dependence*.

Dependence has consequences for rainfall frequency analysis. The station-year method assumes that annual maxima at different sites are independent. It combines records of length M years from N stations to form one record of length MN station-years. If there is dependence, the effective number of independent stations is smaller than N, and so the length of the combined record should be reduced.

Note that although the top point will be plotted at too long a return period using the station-year method, there is some compensation in that the method also plots too many high annual maxima (because it includes several from each event). Thus the station-year assumption leads to uncertainty in the growth curve but not, given a sufficiently long record, to bias (Hosking and Wallis, 1988).

Dales and Reed (1989) developed a model of spatial dependence to estimate the offset distance, $\ln N_e$, for any raingauge network. The UK model relates dependence to the geometry of the raingauge network:

$$\ln N_e / \ln N = 0.081 + 0.085 \ln\text{AREA} - 0.051 \ln N - 0.027 \ln D \qquad (8.3)$$

where N is the number of gauges and D the rainfall duration in days. For sub-daily durations, D is measured in day-equivalents to account for the effect of temporal discretisation. The duration in days is given by the duration in hours divided by 18, for durations shorter than 15 hours (Dales and Reed, 1989).

AREA is a nominal area spanned by the network, evaluated by:

$$\text{AREA} = 2.5\,(\bar{d})^2 \tag{8.4}$$

where $\bar{d}$ denotes the geometric mean inter-gauge distance in kilometres evaluated across all possible pairs of gauges.

The Dales and Reed model was calibrated using data from many networks of raingauges throughout the UK. Dales and Reed (1989) used only daily data, however Stewart *et al.* (1995) showed that the model performs well for sub-daily durations also. The model was used by Reed and Stewart (1989) in the FORGE method of rainfall frequency estimation, and has also been applied and modified for use in Australia (Nandakumar *et al.*, 1997).

The FORGEX method supplies netmax points for use in extending the growth curve to long return periods in a way which parallels the derivation of the spatial dependence model. For each network in turn, the netmax series is constructed and the values ranked. The plotting position of each point incorporates a shift to the right by $\ln N_e$, where N_e is the effective number of independent stations estimated using the Dales and Reed model.

N_e is estimated separately for each netmax point from the characteristics of the gauge network operational in the year concerned. This is important because a network of large diameter can grow from two gauges in the mid 19th century to 1000 gauges in the 1970s (see Figure 14.3). The use of a value of N_e averaged over the period of record would be an unsatisfactory compromise.

The netmax plotting positions, incorporating the N_e adjustment, are derived using a new approach based on maximum likelihood theory, described by Jones (1997). Figure 8.2 includes netmax points, represented by numbers which match the network numbers on Figure 8.1. The netmax points follow on from the pooled points and enable the extension of the growth curve to return periods longer than 1000 years.

8.6 Fitting the growth curve

FORGEX is an empirical method in that the rainfall growth curve is not assumed to follow any particular frequency distribution. The aim is to let the results follow the data, which are plentiful. Any assumption that the data follow a particular distribution would have had a large effect on the estimation of rainfalls with long return periods, and would also have been likely to cause contradictions between growth curves for different rainfall durations.

The rainfall growth curve is represented as a concatenation of linear segments on the Gumbel reduced variate scale. Because of the standardisation by the median, the growth curve is constrained to take the value 1.0 at a return period of two years. Thus fitting the growth curve involves only determining the gradient of each segment. The rules defining the segmentation of the growth curve are explained by Reed *et al.* (1999).

The growth curve is fitted jointly to pooled and network maximum points by a least-squares routine, which has been adapted to encourage smoothness, i.e. avoiding large changes in gradient between adjacent segments. Large changes of gradient between adjacent growth curve segments are undesirable, particularly when they are due to one segment having negative gradient, a feature which occurred in a small number of growth curves before the introduction of smoothing.

The chosen method of smoothing involves moderating the least squares fit by a type of penalty function (see for example Adby and Dempster, 1974). The penalty function is added to the sum of squared differences (between observed and modelled standardised rainfall) to give the following objective function by which the n unknown parameters (gradients of the n segments) are determined:

$$\sum_{1}^{M} (\text{observed}-\text{modelled})^2 + 0.005 \; \frac{M}{n-1} \sum_{j=2}^{M} (a_j-a_{j-1})^2 \qquad (8.5)$$

where M is the total number of pooled and netmax points and a_j is the gradient of the jth segment. The factor 0.05 was chosen experimentally; it provides a degree of smoothing while sustaining characteristic features of the growth curves focused on particular sites.

Figure 8.3 shows the growth curve for 1-day rainfall focused on Leicester, together with the pooled and netmax points. It defines rainfall growth rates for return periods up to 2400 years. In order to avoid excessive reliance on the very highest netmax points, the growth curve is taken to extend only as far as the plotting position of the third highest netmax point in the largest network.

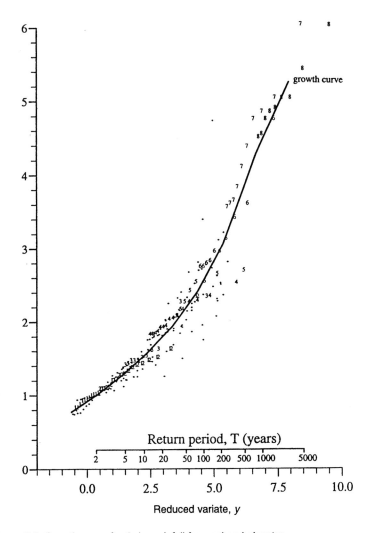

Figure 8.3 Growth curve for 1-day rainfall focused on Leicester

8.7 Assessing the performance of FORGEX

The overall performance of FORGEX at short to medium return periods can be assessed by deriving growth curves for many gauged sites and counting the number of exceedances of the T-year rainfall in the gauged record at each site. Trials indicate a small bias, with 10 to 20 % fewer exceedances observed in sets of 500 records selected at random, than expected according to FORGEX. An overestimation of 15% in frequency corresponds to a typical overestimation of rainfall growth rates of about 4%.

The bias arises in part from the use of netmax points. In cases where no extreme event has been recorded locally, FORGEX provides a netmax point representing an extreme observed in a wider network, which inevitably pulls the growth curve upwards. The bias disappears when the growth curve is re-fitted to the pooled data points alone. This bias is considered beneficial as it recognises that as additional data become available, rainfall growth estimates are more likely to increase than decrease.

Validation of the growth rates at longer return periods may be problematic. Simulation studies are thought to be of limited value because of the difficulty of generating standardised annual maximum rainfalls that exhibit a realistic structure of spatial dependence. However, Nandakumar *et al.* (1997) investigated a spatial dependence model using generated data in which dependence was indexed by correlation coefficient.

Various sensitivity tests on FORGEX are reported by Faulkner and Prudhomme (1997), including examinations of sensitivity to raingauge density and to individual large rainfall events. None of these tests gave any cause for concern. The sensitivity of the results to period of record is examined in the following chapter.

Chapter 9   Confidence limits for growth curves

9.1 Background

There is an increasing demand for measures of confidence to be supplied along with frequency estimates. Confidence limits for rainfall frequency estimates are difficult to quantify because of the number of sources of uncertainty. For example, the FSR volume on rainfall gives no measure of confidence, apart from noting that the station-year method gives estimates at longer return periods "with lesser confidence" (FSR Volume II, Section 2.3).

Confidence limits

Confidence limits give an indication of the range of values in which we expect the true growth rate to lie.

The confidence limits described here measure the uncertainty in growth rates due to the limitations of the sample size. They do not attempt to account for sources of error such as gauging inaccuracies (Section 3.4). The true growth rate could only be known if we had an infinitely long record of rainfall, in which case we could derive the underlying population of annual maxima (assuming no climate change).

Bootstrap methods have been developed relatively recently (Efron, 1979). They enable the derivation of confidence limits and the use of significance tests in situations where the underlying statistical population is unknown, or where confidence limits cannot be obtained by classical analytical techniques.

Bootstrapping

Bootstrapping is so called because it enables information such as confidence limits to be estimated from a sample alone, with no external frame of reference. There are similarities with pulling yourself up by your own bootlaces.

Bootstrapping is based on the generation of many *resamples*, which are selected from the original sample. This sample is used as the distribution from which the resamples are chosen randomly, with each value being returned to the original sample after it has been chosen, so that it may be picked again.

In regional rainfall frequency estimation there are two alternative samples to work with: the years for which data are available or the sites of the gauges. The time domain is more relevant because there is more scope for variation between annual maxima in different years than at different sites, due to spatial dependence. It is easy to imagine an immense rainfall occurring in a year which is just before records start, or just after they end. It is less likely that an isolated storm would be totally missed by the dense (daily) raingauge network in the UK.

9.2 Method: bootstrapping

Resampling takes place using the entire network for a single year as the sampling unit, rather than individual gauge-years. This preserves the spatial dependence which is an inherent and important feature of extreme rainfall which the FORGEX method exploits. The basic method to find the $100(1-2a)$% confidence interval is as follows:

- Draw a resample from the M years providing rainfall data

- Use the resulting at-site records to derive a growth curve with the FORGEX method

- Repeat the above steps 199 times to give 199 growth curves.

- For various return periods, find the bootstrap residuals E_i, which are the deviations of each new growth rate G_i from the original sample growth rate G_{sam}, i.e. $E_i = G_i - G_{sam}$.

- Rank the residuals in ascending order and find E_m and E_n where $m = 199a$ and $n = 200(1-a)$. To obtain 95% confidence limits, the 5th and 195th values are used out of an ordered sample of 199.

- The confidence interval for the unknown growth rate is $(G_{sam} - E_n, G_{sam} - E_m)$.

The assumptions and theory behind this method are treated more fully by Faulkner and Jones (1999). It is important to note that the confidence limits are found by ranking the bootstrap residuals E_i, not the resampled growth rates G_i, which is what one might intuitively expect (compare Figures 9.1 and 9.2: the majority of resampled growth curves lie under the original growth curve, but this growth curve lies nearer to the lower confidence limit) – see also **1** A.3.6.

In practice, the more efficient method of balanced resampling was used. The principle of this method is to ensure that each year occurs equally often overall among the 199 bootstrap samples. This is implemented by creating a series of length $199M$ consisting of the M years of record repeated 199 times. This series is then randomly re-ordered, and divided into slices of length M, to obtain 199 bootstrap samples.

Another modification was to divide the dataset into two eras, before and after 1961. These eras were resampled separately, to preserve the feature of the data illustrated in Figure 14.3: only a small proportion of daily gauges supply data from before 1961.

9.3 Results and discussion

Figure 9.1 shows 199 growth curves for 1-day rainfall focused on Leicester, together with the original growth curve estimated from all the data. The resulting 95% confidence limits, obtained by ranking the bootstrap residuals, are shown in Figure 9.2. The dashed lines connect the results for different return periods. Note that the shape of the confidence limits is a property of the FORGEX method, and in particular the relative contributions of pooled and netmax points at different return periods. For example, the limits are relatively narrow for return periods around 200-500 years, where the growth curve is fitted only to netmax points (Figure 8.2).

The upper limit is typically 0.4 to 0.6 units of standardised rainfall above the growth curve, and the lower limit varies from very close to 0.3 units below.

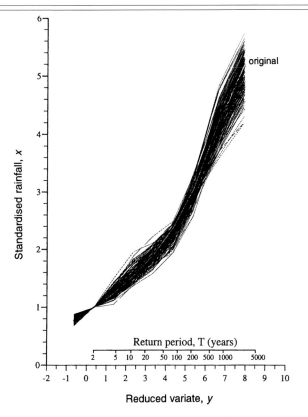

Figure 9.1 *199 resampled 1-day growth curves focused on Leicester*

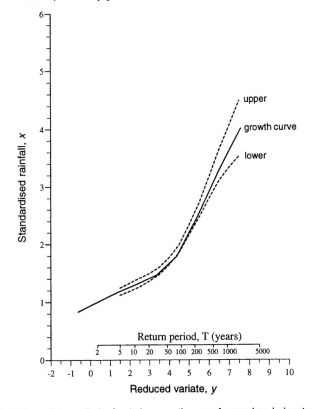

Figure 9.2 95% confidence limits for 1-day growth curve focused on Leicester

The asymmetry is due partly to the upward curvature of the growth curve. This was confirmed by some tests on single-site flood frequency curves with different shapes. It only takes one large event to pull up the growth curve significantly, and so the upper confidence interval is rather large.

Another example, for 1-day rainfall at Kendal in the Lake District, is shown in Figure 9.3. Growth rates at Kendal (for moderate return periods) are among the lowest in the country, and the confidence limits are narrow, only broadening when T exceeds 1000 years. The position of the growth curve within the 95% confidence interval follows the same pattern as for Leicester. The confidence limits are asymmetrical around halfway along the growth curve, where the curvature is strongest.

If Figures 9.2 and 9.3 are superimposed, it can be seen that the confidence intervals for growth curves at Leicester and Kendal do not overlap (for $T>10$ years). Note that this is not a formal test for a significant difference between the growth curves. However, the technique of bootstrapping is a valuable tool for assessing the effect of a limited period of record on growth curve estimation.

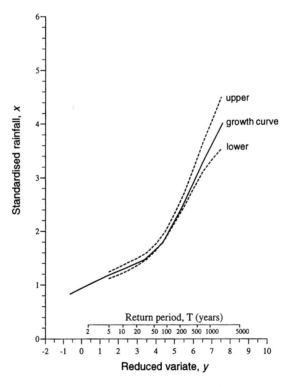

Figure 9.3 *95% confidence limits for 1-day growth curve focused on Kendal*

9.4 Use of confidence intervals

The use of confidence intervals in frequency estimation is a difficult issue. It is good to know the uncertainty associated with any statistical estimate, but the production of a range of design events for every return period could have awkward consequences. It is recommended that the best estimate is used in all cases. Adding safety factors on the basis of confidence intervals creates problems for cost-benefit analysis: it is better to adopt a best estimate of a rarer design event. Confidence intervals can be useful in knowing where rainfall frequency estimates are most uncertain. However, the production of maps of confidence intervals is not computationally feasible at present.

For the above reasons, confidence limits remain a research tool. There is scope to develop methods for confidence interval evaluation that support decision-making more effectively. Confidence intervals for growth rates could eventually be combined with the uncertainty in the index variable RMED to give an overall assessment of uncertainty.

For the time being, the maps of standard deviation of RMED (Figures 7.4 and 7.5) give a good indication of the reliability of estimates, particularly for short return periods, in different parts of the country.

Chapter 10 Building the depth-duration-frequency model

10.1 Requirement for a DDF model

During the mapping of RMED and the derivation of growth curves, each rainfall duration was treated separately. The results were then incorporated into a model linking rainfall depth, duration and frequency (a DDF model). Such a model enables the estimation of rainfall frequency for any intermediate duration. It also allows the extrapolation of rainfall frequency estimates, particularly for durations shorter than 1 day, for which growth curves do not extend to return periods as long as 1000 years. Incorporating information from longer duration rainfall guides what would otherwise be an uncertain extrapolation.

A further reason for requiring a DDF model is to reconcile rainfall estimates for different durations. If each duration is treated separately, it is possible that contradictions between rainfall estimates of different durations could occur, for example if the estimated 2-day 100-year rainfall were smaller than the 1-day 100-year rainfall at the same site (even after accounting for discretisation, see §10.4.1).

The requirements in developing a DDF model were as follows:

- It should provide design rainfall estimates for any duration and return period;

- It should follow local and regional variations in design rainfalls, where possible;

- It must avoid any contradictions between durations or return periods.

Note that a DDF model should not be expected to improve the accuracy of estimating rainfalls for the primary durations at which data are available. Although a model incorporates information from other durations, Buishand (1993) showed that the dependence between annual maxima over different durations is such that little or no improvement can be obtained.

10.2 Form of the DDF model

The DDF model is fitted to an individual site. Design rainfalls, which are products of growth rates from FORGEX and estimates of RMED, are plotted in the depth-duration domain. Depths are adjusted for discretisation before plotting (§10.4.1). An example (for design rainfalls at Waddington in Lincolnshire, grid reference 4988 3653) is shown in Figure 10.1. There are fewer points at long return periods for sub-daily durations because sub-daily growth curves do not extend to such return periods. Note that there are some contradictions between the results for 1-day to 8-day rainfall for return periods longer than 100 years.

A logarithmic scale is used for depth and duration so that, if the depth-duration model is of the form $R = aD^b$, it will plot as a straight line for a given return period. Power laws of this form have been used previously, for instance by Ferreri and Ferro (1990) and Reed and Stewart (1994). Chen (1983) proposed a model with an extra parameter, $R = aD(D+b)^{-c}$, but this is also linear on a logarithmic scale for all but the shortest durations, because $b \ll D$ for durations longer than half an hour. The earlier model developed for the FSR was similar (see Section 10.5).

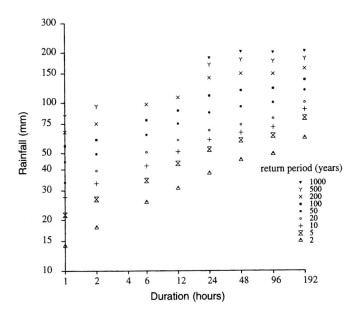

Figure 10.1 *Design rainfalls for Waddington on a DDF plot*

Note that these formulae are often expressed in terms of rainfall intensity rather than rainfall depth over a certain duration. The latter has been chosen for use in the FEH because it is aggregated rainfall depth, rather than instantaneous intensity, that is actually measured and that is of importance for flood estimation.

10.3 Building the model

10.3.1 Description of the six-parameter model

The points in Figure 10.1 do not lie in straight lines for each return period, although fitting a straight line might be a first approximation. It was decided to fit a more flexible function, based on concatenated straight line segments. The model has six parameters. The increase of rainfall with duration is represented by three concatenated line segments, with slopes $a_1(y)$, $a_2(y)$ and $a_3(y)$. The intercept of the first segment on the rainfall axis (where $\ln D = 0$) is denoted $b(y)$. The position of the lines varies with return period, measured by the Gumbel reduced variate y.

The form of the DDF model is illustrated in Figure 10.2, with two separate

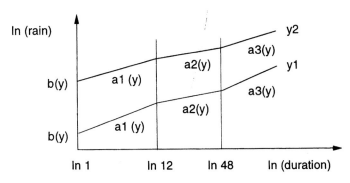

Figure 10.2 *Form of the DDF model*

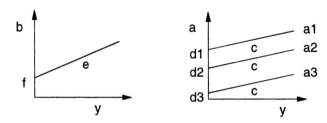

Figure 10.3 *Variation of the parameters a and b with Gumbel reduced variate, y*

lines to illustrate the relationship with frequency. The breaks in slope are at durations of 12 and 48 hours.

The increase of rainfall with return period is represented by a linear variation of a_1, a_2, a_3 and b with y. Figure 10.3 shows the definition of the six parameters which control this variation: c, d_1, d_2, d_3, e and f. These six parameters completely define the DDF model at any location, according to the following formulae:

for $D \leq 12$ hours:

$$\ln R = (cy + d_1) \ln D + ey + f \qquad (10.1)$$

for $12 < D \leq 48$ hours:

$$\ln R = \ln R_{12} + (cy + d_2)(\ln D - \ln 12) \qquad (10.2)$$

for $D > 48$ hours:

$$\ln R = \ln R_{48} + (cy + d_3)(\ln D - \ln 48) \qquad (10.3)$$

Variations on the model were investigated, including simpler versions with only one or two line segments. A more complex version was also tried, with more than one c parameter, allowing the slopes a_i to vary independently with y. The six-parameter model was chosen by comparing the mean squared error from fitting the models to data at several sites.

10.3.2 Choice of the durations at which the slope changes

The choice of the two durations at which the slope changes was made partly on meteorological grounds and partly empirically. A version of the model with breaks in slope at 1 and 3 days was also considered. The final model, with breaks in slope at 12 and 48 hours, is easier to explain on meteorological grounds. For durations shorter than 12 hours, it is likely that many rainfall extremes are due to convective activity. Frontal rainfall is likely to give rise to most extremes for longer durations. Depressions typically pass over Britain in less than two days (Chandler and Gregory, 1976), so it is reasonable to expect a change in the nature of rainfall extreme at about this duration.

The decision to use this model was strengthened when both versions of the model were fitted to data from grid points over all of Britain. The final model has a smaller mean squared error averaged over all locations. Rainfall intensity-duration-frequency diagrams for Australia also change slope at 12 hours (Institute of Engineers, Australia, 1987).

It is possible that in reality the durations D_1 and D_2 at which the nature of extreme rainfall changes may vary with return period. For example, a set of convective storm cells is unlikely to give heavy rainfall persisting over many hours, but could do so in an extreme case, which would give a long return period rainfall. However, introducing this extra degree of freedom would increase the number of parameters in the model, and also make contradictions harder to avoid (see §10.4.2).

10.3.3 Comment on the variation of depth with return period

The DDF model imposes a functional form on the relationship between rainfall and return period. This is an exponential curve on the Gumbel reduced variate scale, as $\ln R$ is proportional to Gumbel reduced variate y.

Figure 10.4 shows a rainfall frequency curve for 1-day rainfall at Leicester, which is rebuilt from the parameters of the DDF model at this site. For comparison, the original FORGEX growth curve is also plotted, scaled up by RMED. The two curves agree closely at all return periods. This is a particularly good example, and at other sites where the FORGEX growth curve is less smooth, the exponential DDF curve does not capture all the detail of the FORGEX curve, which is composed of linear segments which can follow the data more closely.

In constructing a consistent DDF model it is necessary to impose a functional form on the rainfall-frequency relationship. It might be argued that it would be better to use the same functional form earlier in the rainfall frequency analysis. However, it is worth retaining the priority given to following the data in the FORGEX method.

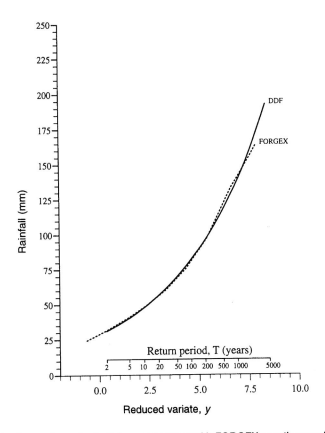

Figure 10.4 *Comparison of rebuilt frequency curve with FORGEX growth curve for 1-day rainfall at Leicester*

10.4 Fitting the model

At each site on a 1-km grid over the UK the DDF model is fitted jointly to rainfalls for all durations (1, 2, 6, 12 hours and 1, 2, 4, 8 days) and return periods (2, 5, 10, 20, 50, 100, 200, 500 and 1000 years) at once, using a least-squares criterion.

Figure 10.5 shows the model fitted to rainfall frequency results at Waddington. The model lines pass very close to some design rainfalls at this site, while others appear to be under- or over-estimated. However, it is important to remember that the design rainfalls are not perfect, for example for T = 200 years, the 4-day rainfall appears to be smaller than the 2-day rainfall. The DDF model resolves these contradictions and smooths out any unwarranted discontinuities in the results. Figure 10.5 illustrates the role of the model in guiding the extrapolation of short-duration results to longer return periods: it enables the estimation of the 1-hour rainfall with return period 1000 years.

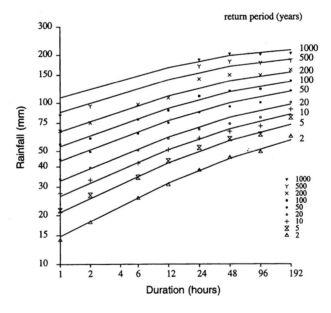

Figure 10.5   *DDF model fitted to design rainfalls for Waddington*

10.4.1 Allowing for discretisation

In reconciling rainfall estimates for different durations, adjustments are required to take account of discretisation. For example, design rainfalls based on 1-day annual maxima are not expected to be as large as those based on 24-hour annual maxima, where the period of 24 hours can start at any hour. Rainfall durations which start and finish at 9 a.m. or at clock hours are referred to as *fixed* durations. Those which can start at any time are referred to as *sliding* durations.

All design rainfalls to which the DDF model is fitted are converted from fixed to sliding durations, using standard conversion factors taken from Dwyer and Reed (1995). The multiplication factors are shown in Table 10.1.

Table 10.1 *Factors used to convert fixed-duration to sliding-duration rainfalls*

Rainfall measured daily		Rainfall measured hourly	
Duration (days)	Multiply by	Duration (hours)	Multiply by
1	1.16	1	1.16
2	1.11	2	1.08
4	1.05	4	1.03
8	1.01	16	1.01
		≥12	1.00

10.4.2 Avoiding contradictions

The DDF model must avoid any contradictions between durations, which would occur if a line on the depth-duration scale has negative gradient, or between return periods, which would occur if two lines for different return periods intersected.

To avoid contradictions between durations, the gradient a_i of each segment of the rain-duration relationship (Figure 10.2) should be positive, and $cy + d_i > 0$ for $i = 1, 2, 3$. In fact c is always negative, so if this condition is satisfied for one value of y, it will be satisfied for all smaller values. Therefore it is sufficient to check that the condition is met for the largest value of y likely to be required. The longest return period likely to be of interest is 10 000 years, which corresponds to a Gumbel reduced variate (y) of 9.21.

So to avoid contradictions between durations, one must ensure that

$$9.21c + d_i > 0 \qquad (10.1)$$

When the model is fitted without the imposition of any constraints, this condition is satisfied at most grid points, but violated at approximately 4% of sites. The final fitting of the model uses an algorithm which ensures that Equation 10.1 is satisfied. Results at most locations are unaffected by the change of algorithm.

To avoid contradictions between return periods, R must increase with y:

$$\frac{\partial(\ln R)}{\partial x} > 0$$

For the first segment, ($D < 12$ hours), this yields $c \ln D + e > 0$. For the other segments, the terms involving 12 and 48 hours cancel out, so the same condition is required for $0 \leq D \leq 192$ hours. Since c happens to be negative everywhere, it is sufficient to ensure that:

$$c \ln 192 + e > 0 \qquad (10.2)$$

This condition is satisfied at all locations.

10.5 Note on the FSR model for M5 rainfall

A model for $M5$ (5-year return period) rainfall was used to smooth the Flood Studies Report rainfall frequency results across durations (FSR Volume II, §3.3.3). The model, which applies for durations up to 2 days, is:

$$I = \frac{I_0}{(1+BD)^n} \qquad\qquad (10.3)$$

where I is the rainfall intensity (i.e. R/D), D the duration in hours, and I_0, B and n are parameters indexed by the annual average rainfall, $SAAR_{4170}$. Because the value of B ranges from 15 to 45, for durations longer than 1 hour, $BD \gg 1$. Thus, apart from a gentle inflection at short durations, the model is essentially a straight line on a logarithmic plot, with gradient $1-n$:

$$\ln R \approx \ln I_0 - n \ln B + (1-n)\ln D \quad \text{for } D > 1 \qquad\qquad (10.4)$$

Values of $M5$ for durations longer than two days are found by interpolation of the results in Table 3.2 of Volume II of the FSR.

The FSR model for $M5$ has a similar form to the DDF model described in the previous section. However, it applies only to 5-year rainfalls, up to a duration of 2 days. Design rainfalls taken from the FSR for longer return periods and longer durations show relationships with duration similar to those found for the new results.

10.6 DDF parameters for points and catchments throughout the UK

Grids of point DDF parameters were constructed by fitting the DDF model to maps of design rainfalls, some examples of which are given in Chapter 11. The grids of DDF parameters are provided on the FEH CD-ROM.

For estimating catchment rainfall it is necessary to know the rainfall for a typical point in a catchment. This can be found from DDF model parameters which are appropriate for the catchment. Note that the rainfall for a typical point does not necessarily translate into the runoff for a typical point, particularly in catchments with variable relief or soils, where the runoff from a portion of the catchment may dominate the flood response.

The rainfall for a typical point in a catchment is most accurately defined as the average of the design rainfalls at each point in the catchment. The most accurate way to find the DDF parameters appropriate for a catchment is therefore to find the average of the design rainfalls at each point in the catchment, for all durations and return periods, and then fit the DDF model to the catchment-average rainfalls. The resulting parameters may not necessarily be identical to the simple catchment average of the point DDF parameters.

The two approaches (sketched in the box) were compared for trial areas of different sizes, and it was found that the resulting DDF parameters were not significantly different. The catchment DDF parameters are therefore calculated by simple averaging of point parameters, as this method is computationally easier.

The FEH CD-ROM provides values of the six parameters of the DDF model for all UK catchments draining an area of at least 0.5 km². At each 50 m grid point draining the required area, a catchment boundary was derived using the digital terrain model (DTM) and overlaid on the 1-km grids of DDF parameters. The resulting catchment parameters are used, along with an areal reduction factor, in estimating catchment design rainfalls for the rainfall-runoff method.

Two routes to obtaining DDF model parameters for a catchment

DDF parameters on a 1-km grid over the catchment

↓

Find design rainfall at each grid point for all
durations and return periods

↓   ↓

Find catchment average
of parameters

Find catchment average of all design rainfalls

↓

Fit DDF model to catchment-average rainfalls   ↓

↓

DDF parameters appropriate for the catchment

Chapter 11 Final maps of rainfall frequency results

11.1 Introduction

The methods described in Chapters 7 to 10 have been applied to produce rainfall frequency results on a 1-km grid covering the UK. The choice of resolution is linked to the use of a 1-km digital terrain model for mapping RMED, and that resolution was chosen for practical and scientific reasons. A scale of 1 km can represent topographic effects in detail, yet avoids attempting to represent microclimatic features of rainfall, which are not desirable or feasible in a nation-wide study of extreme rainfall.

In some situations the scale of 1 km is rather finer than is justified by the data or the methods. For example, 1000-year growth rates are estimated from very large networks of rain gauges, and any significant variations in these on the scale of a few km are unlikely to be genuine. However, the resulting design rainfall may vary over a short distance due to genuine differences in the index rainfall, RMED.

Example maps of growth rates and design rainfalls are presented in Sections 11.2 and 11.3. The final results which enable the estimation of point rainfall frequency anywhere in the UK are grids of DDF model parameters, provided on the FEH CD-ROM.

11.2 Maps of growth rates

These maps were constructed by running the FORGEX algorithms for each rainfall duration at every grid point across the UK. Growth rates for several return periods were estimated for each site. The production of each map involved a tremendous number of calculations, and some approximations were made to enable the completion of the task within a reasonable time. Figures 11.1 and 11.2 are examples of the results: maps of 100-year rainfall growth rates for durations of 1 day and 1 hour.

11.2.1 1-day growth rates

The 100-year growth rate for 1-day rainfall (Figure 11.1) shows a general increase from the north and west to the east and south. The pattern for other return periods is similar. The largest 1-day growth rates are in four areas of England: Somerset, the Fens of Cambridgeshire and Lincolnshire, east Norfolk and north Kent. The influence of notable storms can be traced in these results. For example at Ditchingham in east Norfolk on 31 August 1994 there was a daily total of 144 mm, and at West Stourmouth, north Kent, on 20 September 1973 there was a total of 191 mm. The effect of the largest daily rainfall in the database can be seen in the south of Dorset, where there is a local increase in the growth rate around Martinstown, with 241 mm recorded (at Upwey) on 18 July 1955.

The smallest 1-day growth rates are found in north-west England, particularly Lancashire and Cumbria, as reported by Dales and Reed (1989). Growth rates are also relatively gentle in western Scotland, south Wales and Hampshire. Rainfall growth rates are generally smaller in the west because of the predominance of frontal rainfall, which tends to give rise to moderate annual maxima but few very large extremes. Conversely, in the east and parts of the south, many 1-day annual maxima are due to convective rainfall which can produce occasional outstanding annual maxima which are several times larger than the median. This relatively dry part of the country shows a more continental behaviour.

Such a division of the country into different rainfall regimes is reflected in the seasonality of rainfall extremes. In Scotland and Wales most 1-day rainfall extremes occur during late autumn and winter, whereas in most of England the average date is in summer and early autumn.

Growth rates tend to be largest in areas where RMED is smallest (see Figure 7.2), because an annual maximum of a given size translates to a higher standardised rainfall if the standardising variable, RMED, is small. There is therefore a limited cancelling-out of regional differences when growth rates are multiplied by RMED to give the design rainfall estimates.

11.2.2   1-hour growth rates

Hourly growth rates are generally larger than daily growth rates, as there is more scope for variation in short-duration annual maxima (imagine a series of annual maximum 6-month rainfalls: they would all be rather similar).

The 100-year growth rate for 1-hour rainfall (Figure 11.2) is large (>3.6) over much of southern and eastern Britain and small (<3.2) in the north, but there are exceptions to this overall pattern. The largest peaks in the growth rate (which are also evident for other return periods) are in Greater London and the Home Counties, Lancashire and north Wales. There are also high growth rates in much of Lincolnshire, the West Midlands and County Londonderry. The smallest growth rates are in coastal areas of northern Scotland. Some parts of the map such as the Western Isles and part of Devon are blank due to a lack of long rainfall records: the 1-hour growth curves do not extend to 100 years in these areas.

Some of the areas with high growth rates have unusually large annual maximum 1-hour rainfalls at several gauges. The growth rates in Londonderry are large because of three notable annual maxima which were all observed at the same gauge (Ballykelly) in 1947, 1949 and 1953. It is difficult to find a single characteristic that the areas of high growth rates have in common: Greater London and the West Midlands are extensive built-up areas; north Wales, Lancashire and Londonderry include upland areas; and Lincolnshire is rural and lowland. The peaks in growth rate are probably due to several meteorological factors.

Although the peaks may look dramatic, the nationwide variation in growth rates is significantly smaller than the variation in RMED. The 1-hour 100-year growth rate varies over the UK from 2.6 to 4.2, whereas the 1-hour RMED (Figure 7.3) varies from approximately 7 mm to over 17 mm. Thus the combined maps of design rainfall in the following section resemble the RMED maps more closely than the growth rate maps. Note that hourly growth rates are not always large where 1-hour RMED is small.

The linear features in remote areas on Figure 11.2 are lines of equidistance between two gauges, where there is a discontinuity in the growth rate.

11.3 Maps of design rainfalls

Maps of RMED (such as Figures 7.2 and 7.3) and growth rates were multiplied to produce grids of design rainfall for various durations and return periods. The DDF model was fitted to these grids, combining all durations and return periods. This section discusses some of the final results, maps of design rainfall estimated by the DDF model. Examples are shown in Figures 11.3 to 11.6, maps of 1-day and

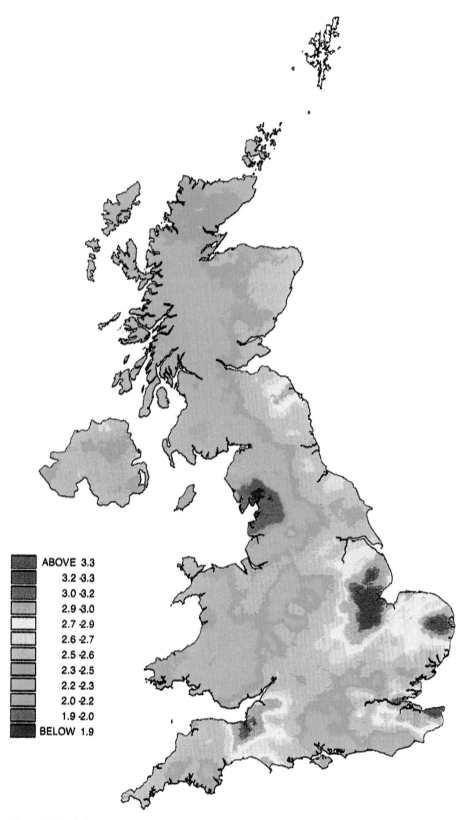

Figure 11.1 *1-day growth rate for T = 100 years*

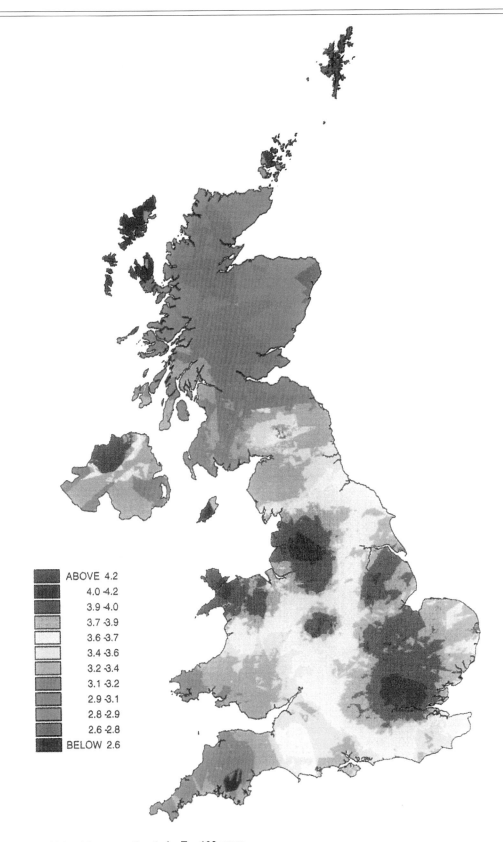

Figure 11.2 *1-hour growth rate for T = 100 years*

1-hour rainfall for 10 and 100 years.

Design rainfalls for the 1-day duration (Figures 11.3 and 11.4) show very similar patterns for return periods of 10 and 100 years, although the influence of the high 100-year return periods in parts of eastern England (see Figure 11.1) is discernible in Figure 11.4. The maps follow the distribution of RMED (Figure 7.2) very closely, with large rainfall totals in western upland areas. The driest areas are in East Anglia, Shropshire, parts of north-west England and central Scotland. Note that the effect of the Martinstown storm is barely discernable, compared with the growth rate map (Figure 11.1). The storm does have a greater effect on rarer design rainfalls: the 1000-year rainfall is up to 200 mm around Martinstown, and 135-150 mm in the surrounding area.

Maps of 1-hour design rainfalls (Figures 11.5 and 11.6) also behave similarly for different return periods. Rainfalls are high in western mountainous areas, also in the Greater London area and the East Midlands, where both RMED and the growth rate are relatively large. The smallest design rainfalls, below 23 mm, are in eastern Scotland, where low growth rates are reinforced by some of the smallest values of RMED. The smallest rainfalls for England and Wales are in Hampshire and the Welsh borders.

11.4   Comparison with previous results

The detail of these maps is striking when compared with the general advice given earlier this century. Bilham (1935) advised that short-duration rainfall appears to be distributed without regard to the average annual rainfall: "on the evidence available up to the present, he would be a bold man who would base designs involving a large capital expenditure on the assumption that his particular area was less subject to intense rainfalls than the hypothetical 'average station' to which our calculations apply". By the 1960s it was thought that upland locations experienced more short-duration extremes than elsewhere (Holland, 1968).

The FSR rainfall frequency statistics were presented as contoured maps. The amount of detail and regional variation was less than that of the new results, and that is one of the principal differences between FEH and FSR rainfall results. The FSR rainfalls have been used for many designs since 1975, so a comparison of FEH and FSR results is of interest.

Figures 11.7 and 11.8 are maps of the ratio of FEH to FSR rainfalls, for a return period of 100 years and durations of 1 day and 1 hour. The maps are based on digitised versions of the FSR maps: Northern Ireland is excluded because digitised FSR results are not available. The FEH results are the final design rainfalls produced from the DDF model, which are spatially smoother than the maps in Figures 11.3 to 11.6, which are simply the products of the grids of growth rate and RMED.

For the 1-day duration (Figure 11.7), the FEH rainfalls are similar to the FSR results over much of Great Britain. The new results are larger (sometimes by as much as 40%) in upland areas and (by 20-30%) in Somerset, the East Midlands and south-east England. An increase of 20-30% in design rainfalls corresponds to a decrease of around half in estimated return periods of events: i.e. storms that were previously assessed as 100-year events will now be allocated a return period of 50 years. FEH rainfalls are smaller in parts of the Welsh and Scottish borders, Cumbria and in parts of central and northern Scotland. The ratios vary most in mountainous areas where the FEH results follow the topography much more closely.

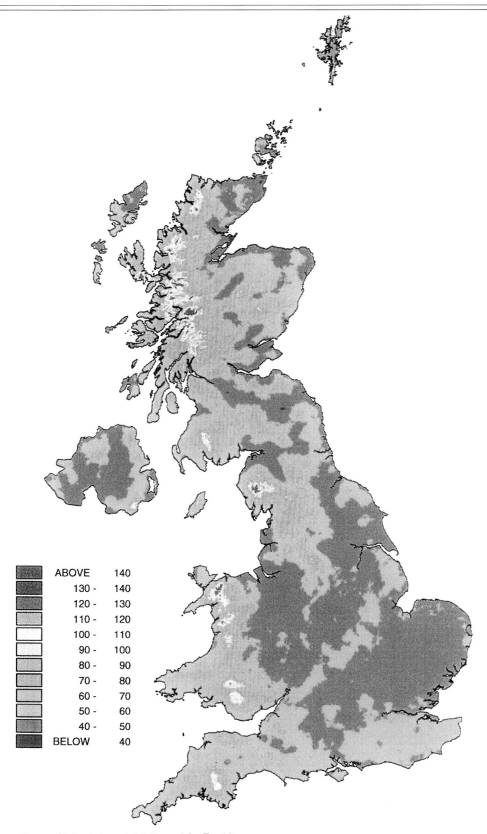

	ABOVE	140
	130 -	140
	120 -	130
	110 -	120
	100 -	110
	90 -	100
	80 -	90
	70 -	80
	60 -	70
	50 -	60
	40 -	50
	BELOW	40

Figure 11.3   1-day rainfall (in mm) for T = 10 years

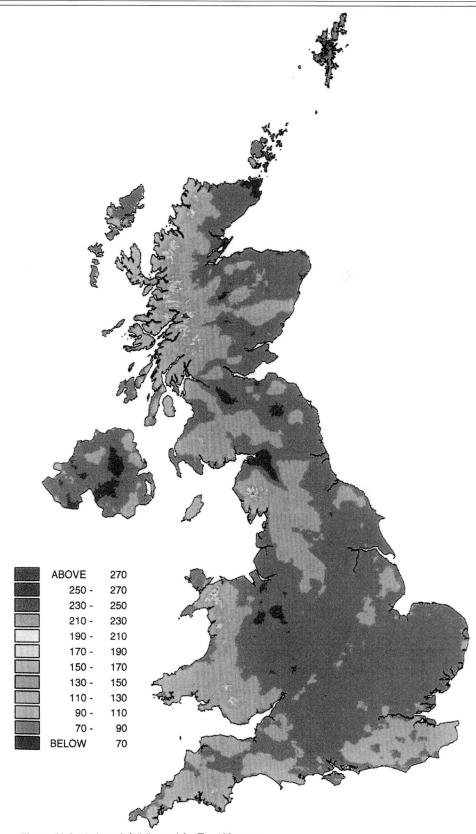

Figure 11.4 *1-day rainfall (in mm) for T = 100 years*

ABOVE		270
250	-	270
230	-	250
210	-	230
190	-	210
170	-	190
150	-	170
130	-	150
110	-	130
90	-	110
70	-	90
BELOW		70

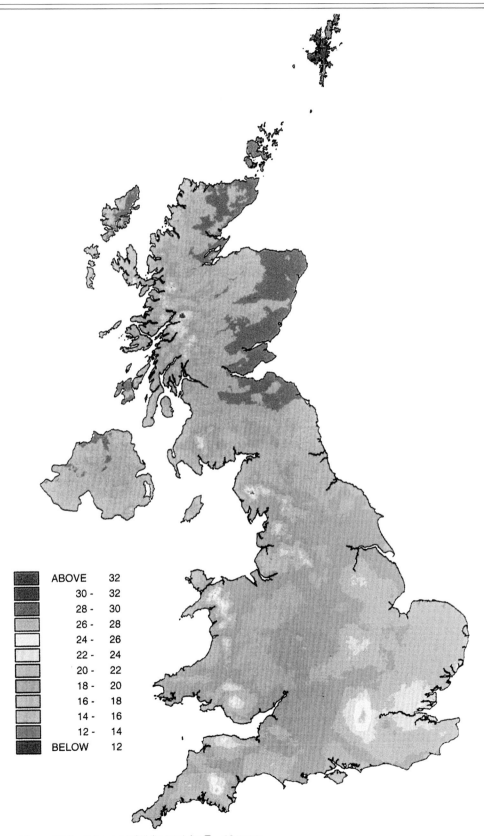

	ABOVE	32
	30 -	32
	28 -	30
	26 -	28
	24 -	26
	22 -	24
	20 -	22
	18 -	20
	16 -	18
	14 -	16
	12 -	14
	BELOW	12

Figure 11.5 *1-hour rainfall (in mm) for T = 10 years*

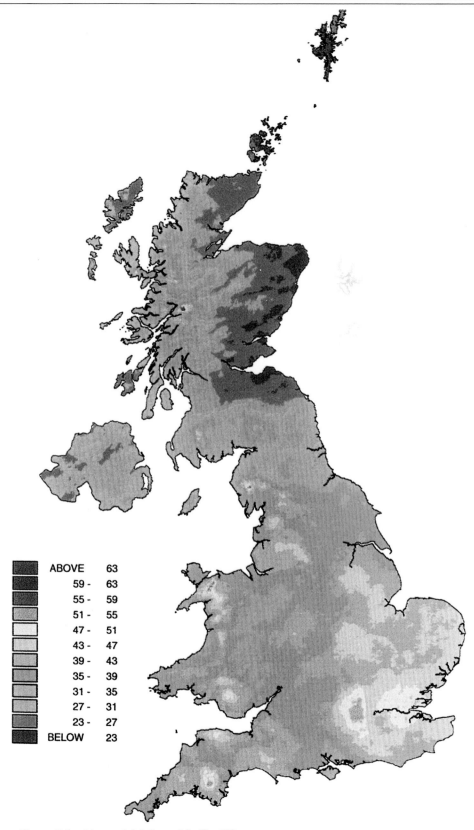

Figure 11.6   *1-hour rainfall (in mm) for T = 100 years*

	ABOVE	63
	59 -	63
	55 -	59
	51 -	55
	47 -	51
	43 -	47
	39 -	43
	35 -	39
	31 -	35
	27 -	31
	23 -	27
	BELOW	23

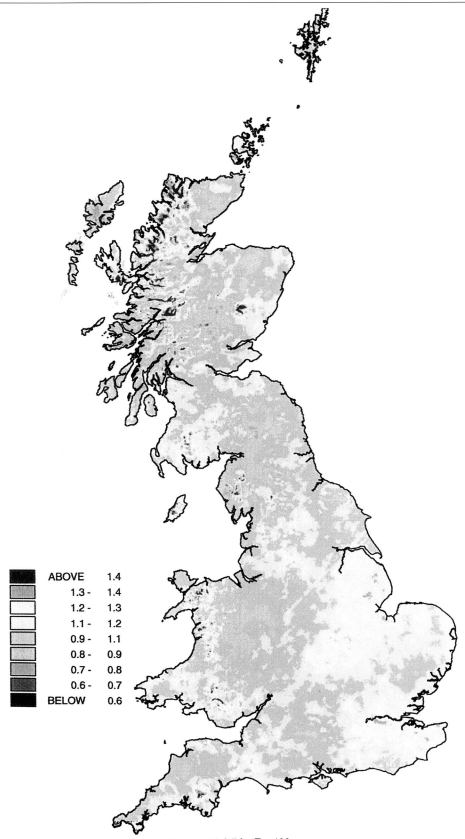

	ABOVE	1.4
	1.3 -	1.4
	1.2 -	1.3
	1.1 -	1.2
	0.9 -	1.1
	0.8 -	0.9
	0.7 -	0.8
	0.6 -	0.7
	BELOW	0.6

Figure 11.7 *Ratio of FEH to FSR 1-day rainfall for T = 100 years*

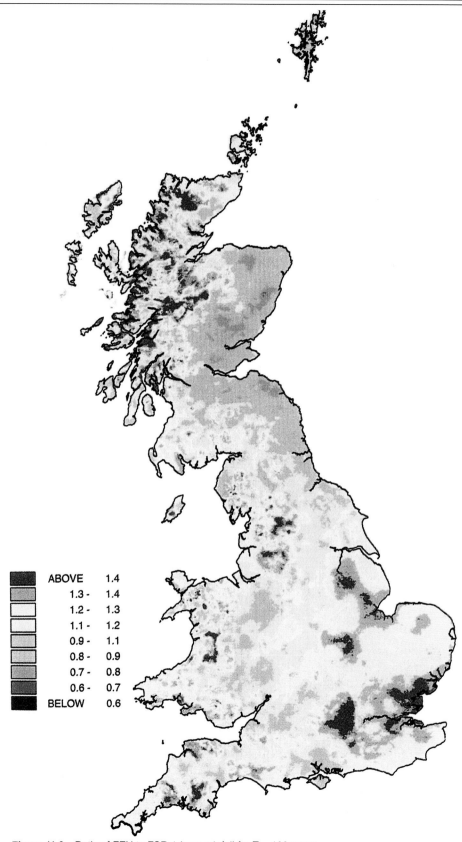

Figure 11.8 Ratio of FEH to FSR 1-hour rainfall for T = 100 years

The legend shows:

ABOVE	1.4
1.3 -	1.4
1.2 -	1.3
1.1 -	1.2
0.9 -	1.1
0.8 -	0.9
0.7 -	0.8
0.6 -	0.7
BELOW	0.6

The new 1-hour rainfalls for a return period of 100 years (Figure 11.8) are larger over much of Great Britain, and over 30% larger in parts of south-east England, the East Midlands and western upland areas. The difference in south-east England rises to 60% in a small part of Berkshire. FEH rainfalls are smaller (by 20-30%) in eastern Scotland and parts of Cumbria and Northumberland. The difference between the east and west coasts of Scotland is striking. For shorter return periods, the ratios are smaller: for T=5 years, FEH rainfalls are similar to or slightly smaller than FSR rainfalls in many places. In the south-east, FEH results for T=5 years are 10-30% higher.

The rainfall growth factors in the FSR appear to be over-general, masking important local and regional variations in rainfall. The FEH procedure takes more account of local data, both in constructing the focused growth curves, and in mapping the standardising variable, RMED.

Chapter 12 Guidance on using the results

12.1 Validity of results for very short or long durations

The DDF model is fitted to rainfalls with durations from 1 hour to 8 days. Rainfall frequency estimates outside this range will sometimes be required, particularly for the design and analysis of sewerage systems which drain small, quickly-responding urban areas. Some extrapolation of the results is justified, particularly since the 1-hour data are relatively plentiful compared with other sub-daily durations. It is unlikely that the processes governing half-hour extreme rainfalls are very different to those governing 1-hour extremes, so the results can be relied on for durations as short as 30 minutes.

The Wallingford Procedure for sewer design and analysis (DOE, 1981) incorporates the FSR rainfall frequency analysis, which included some data for durations as short as 15 seconds. The Wallingford Procedure uses FSR results for rainfall durations down to 5 minutes. If the FEH results are extrapolated to 15 minutes and mapped, it will be seen that they generally agree well with the FSR results for the same duration, with only a few local differences. Nevertheless, there is scope for further research on the frequency of sub-hourly rainfalls (Faulkner, 1998), for which tipping bucket recorders (see Chapter 13) provide one source of useful data.

Occasionally rainfall estimates may be required for durations longer than 8 days, for example in analysing the frequency of long-duration rainfall totals which contribute to flooding on permeable catchments where the flood regime is groundwater-dominated. The FSR analysis included 25-day and 1-month annual maximum rainfalls, which were used to produce a map of 25-day $M5$ as a percentage of $SAAR_{4170}$. An equivalent map extrapolated from the FEH analysis differs significantly, yielding lower values than the FSR estimates. It is therefore recommended that the FSR map continues to be used to estimate 25-day extreme rainfall totals, until this can be studied further.

12.2 Using additional local data

The ideal situation for rainfall frequency estimation would be to have at least 1000 years of rainfall data at the site of interest. Assuming there was no trend over such a long period, and that rain gauging in the 10th century was of a similar standard to today, this immense record could be used to derive locally appropriate rainfall estimates for long return periods.

Unfortunately no such records exist, and so data from other sites are used to guide the estimation of rare rainfalls. Where users have access to rainfall records of a more realistic length (even 50-100 years), it is recommended in most cases that local data analyses should not be used to adjust the FEH rainfall frequency results. A similar recommendation was made by the FSR (Volume II, Section 1.13). The reason that this advice differs from that given in flood frequency estimation is that rainfall is a much more spatially consistent variable than river flow, affected less by local features. The addition of local rainfall records is therefore much less likely to significantly improve an estimate than the addition of local flow records.

The area where local rainfall records are most likely to be valuable is in the estimation of RMED. The addition of annual maximum series to fill in some of the gaps in the recording raingauge network (for example in the west of Scotland) would be particularly valuable. The adjustment of rainfall growth curves with local data is not recommended, as the FORGEX method relies on regional data, including some very long series.

12.3 Fluctuations, trends and climate change

The mention of return periods as long as 2000 years inevitably attracts a question along the lines of "You don't even know what the climate will be like in 50 years, so how can you talk about 2000-year return periods?". The first part of dealing with such questions must be to emphasise that return periods should be viewed as probabilities rather than long-term predictions. There is a 0.0005 probability that the 2000-year rainfall will be exceeded next year. Another important point to understand is the distinction between climate fluctuations and climate trends.

Inevitably there will be periods when clusters of extreme rainfalls occur. For example at Northmoor near Bridgwater in Devon, a 1-day rainfall of 115 mm on 10 July 1968 was followed a year later by a total of 92 mm on 28 July 1969. The FEH-assessed return periods of these events are 475 years and 160 years respectively. Scepticism about such quoted return periods is perhaps understandable among local residents suffering the consequences of two such extreme rainfalls in successive years. However, such fluctuations must be distinguished from long-term climate trends, which would require rainfall frequency estimates to be amended. Periodic variations in extreme hourly rainfalls with periods of 7, 11, 20 and 50 years have been described by May and Hitch (1989a). Trends in the FEH rainfall data are examined in Section 14.3.

The estimation of the index rainfall, RMED, is potentially susceptible to climatic fluctuations, which may cause estimates to be affected by the period of record. The required minimum record length of 9 years should help to smooth out short-period variations. Further smoothing is provided by the use of kriging as an interpolation technique, which combines data from several nearby sites. Because there are relatively few rainfall records longer than 30 years (particularly for sub-daily durations), it would be difficult to account for any long-period variations without using data from further afield than is desirable.

Regarding long-term climatic trends, the current hot topic is global warming due to emission of greenhouse gases. Little is currently known about the effect of global warming on rainfall frequency, as most studies of the impacts of global warming have looked at likely changes in the means rather than the extremes of climate. It is particularly difficult to examine the impact of global warming on rainfall on a daily or shorter time-scale, as the size of the grid cells used in global circulation models (GCMs) is much larger than convective elements in the atmosphere.

The 1996 report of the Intergovernmental Panel on Climate Change (IPCC, 1996) stated that there is now mounting evidence that a warmer climate will be one in which the hydrological cycle will be more intense, leading to more heavy rain events. For example, Gregory and Mitchell (1995) examined the daily variability of precipitation in Europe using the UK Hadley Centre GCM. They found a significant increase in the summer mean maximum daily rainfall in England, given a doubling of the concentration of CO_2 in the atmosphere. In the simulated climate, precipitation is distributed over fewer days with relatively larger daily amounts.

Another study (CCIRG, 1996) suggested that the average intensity of precipitation will increase modestly by the 2020s in all seasons for all regions of the UK. It is possible that return periods of heavy daily rainfall events will shorten, especially over the north of the country in the summer. This scenario was based on the results from an earlier version of the Hadley Centre GCM.

As the resolution of GCMs improves, and better techniques for disaggregating the output of GCMs become available, more confidence will be attached to assessments of the impact of global warming on rainfall frequency. It is possible that guidelines for adjusting rainfall frequency estimates will be produced in the future.

12.4 Seasonal maximum rainfalls and types of rainfall events

There is some demand for seasonal design rainfalls, for example in agriculture, construction projects and the design of some urban pollution control systems that are only likely to be tested in one season.

The seasonal distribution of UK rainfall extremes has been examined by mapping the mean occurrence date of 1-day rainfall peaks over a threshold. Seasonality is represented by circular statistics: a rainfall event is represented by a vector of unit length radiating in a direction corresponding to the time of year. The results are shown in Figure 12.1. Each dot is the location of a raingauge, and the tail lies in the direction representing the mean occurrence date. The thickness of the tail denotes the seasonal concentration: it is proportional to the mean resultant length of the unit vectors.

The mean occurrence date shows a remarkable pattern. In the north and west of Britain, extreme rainfalls occur mostly during late autumn and winter whereas in the east, the date of appearance changes to summer and early autumn. This is presumably due to the division between frontal rainfall which predominates in the west and convective rainfall which is more typical of the east and occurs mainly in the summer. The regions of differing seasonality are divided by relatively clear lines in some areas, such as the Cambrian mountains. The area to the east of Wales is in the lee of the Cambrian mountains and receives only a small amount of frontal precipitation. At the same time the mountains are an obstacle for thunderstorms moving from the east.

Dales and Reed (1989) compiled monthly distributions of annual maximum 1-day rainfalls for regions of England and Wales. The mean date of annual maxima ranges from mid-August, in eastern and central England, to late October, in southwest England (Dales and Reed, 1989). The seasonal effect is strongest in central and eastern England, which experience more than one third of their annual maxima in July and August, when convective storms are most frequent.

Because of the strong regional signature of seasonal effects, any analysis of seasonal maxima would need to be done for the whole country. In addition, there are different ways to divide the year into seasons, for example four seasons or just winter and summer. A seasonal version of the FEH results would entail repeating the entire analysis for each definition of the seasons. Tabony (1983) considered the analysis of monthly meteorological extremes and concluded that the use of annual maxima is often to be preferred, to avoid the inclusion of insufficiently extreme monthly observations.

Some work on seasonal rainfall frequency has been carried out in the past. Dales and Reed (1989) abstracted summer and winter annual maximum 1-day rainfalls for England and Wales and fitted growth curves. They found that summer rainfall events dominate in determining the all-year growth curve, especially at long return periods. Similar results were found for shorter-duration extremes in the FSR (Volume II, Section 3.4). The FSR includes seasonal adjustments for the index rainfall, $M5$, but does not give any guidance on their use. Metcalfe (1994) discusses the estimation of short-term *flood* risk, incorporating seasonal variation. His model may be of interest to contractors working in rivers, or engineers responsible for operating reservoirs.

The analysis of seasonal maxima is a step towards linking rainfall frequency with meteorology, as different types of rainfall events dominate at different times of year. There is scope for further research into this, unscrambling the problem of growth curves that arise from mixed distributions (Faiers *et al.*, 1994).

The annual maximum approach used in the FEH analysis can give rise to 8-day annual maxima consisting of only one or two wet days that contain a very extreme storm. It is unfortunate that 8-day design rainfalls can be derived from 1-day storms, which are likely to arise from different meteorological processes. It is sometimes suggested that one should analyse storms rather than fixed-duration rainfall accumulations. However, flood-producing rainfalls are catchment rainfalls and not storms. They may represent a whole storm, half a storm or two storms, an unusually stationary storm, a passing squall, a multi-cellular thunderstorm or a small part of widespread frontal rainfall. It is this richness of scenarios, coupled with the requirement to make frequency statements, that encourages a statistical analysis of extreme gauged rainfall depths rather than a meteorological study of storm properties.

Figure 12.1   *Seasonality of extreme rainfall*

Chapter 13 Gathering and quality control of rainfall data

13.1 Requirement

The gathering of rainfall data was a major part of the rainfall frequency research. Series of annual maximum rainfalls for durations between 1 hour and 8 days were sought from raingauges throughout the UK. The growth curve analysis was restricted to records at least ten years long; however, some shorter records were also included in the database.

Some records were obtained directly from suppliers as annual maximum series; others were abstracted from continuous daily or hourly data, or times of tip from tipping bucket recorders. A survey of rainfall data in England and Wales (Stewart and Reynard, 1994) included the possibility of using weather radar data. Rainfall estimates from weather radar have the advantages of a high resolution in space and time, and they are able to represent areal rather than merely point rainfall. However, radar data would have been able to contribute only fairly short records to the study, and would have raised difficult issues of calibration, quality control and combination with raingauge data.

13.2 Sources of data

The UK network of daily raingauges is dense, as shown by Figure 13.1, which is a map of all gauges providing at least ten annual maxima. The only major gap is in the Outer Hebrides. The best-gauged areas are Greater London and the Pennines above Manchester, where there are many reservoirs.

The vast majority of daily annual maxima were abstracted from computerised records provided by the Met. Office. The total number of records at least ten years long is approximately 6100, including a set of 561 long-term records with data from before 1961, shown on Figure 13.2. The Irish Met. Service provided data for 30 daily gauges close to the border with Northern Ireland. A few records of daily annual maxima were also provided by the Climatological Observers Link.

Most long-term daily and all sub-daily data from the Met. Office and the Environment Agency were made available to the study under the terms of Memoranda of Understanding. These agreements define the contributions to the study of the Met. Office, the Institute of Hydrology and (for England and Wales) the Environment Agency, and restrict the use of the data. Sub-daily rainfall measurements were received from many sources throughout the UK, in 19 different formats: the organisations providing data are listed here.

The *Met. Office* provided continuous hourly records from 107 gauges, including eight in Northern Ireland. Most of these span the 1980s and 1990s, with some extending back to the 1970s. Several of the records for Northern Ireland were obtained by digitising charts from tilting syphon rainfall recorders. A computer archive of 1-hour annual maximum rainfalls compiled by May and Hitch (1989b) at the Met. Office provided the greatest number of records: 159 throughout the UK. This archive includes the 1-hour annual maxima used in the FSR analysis, as well as more recent data. Some records extend back to the 19th century. Annual maxima for longer durations — tabulated as part of the FSR research — were retrieved from the Met. Office archive and typed into computer files at IH, adding 99 gauges to the total. These series are of varying lengths, ceasing in 1971.

Figure 13.1 *Locations of daily gauges*

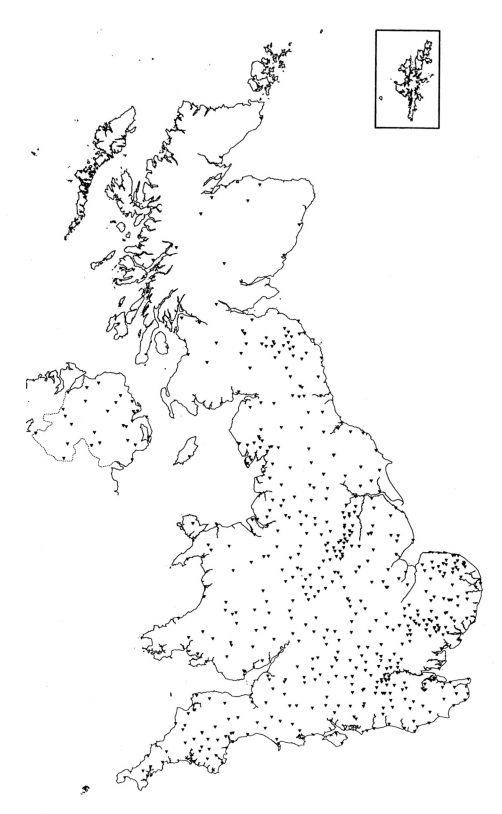

Figure 13.2 *Locations of long-term daily gauges*

The *Environment Agency* provided data from 135 recording raingauges in a variety of formats. The largest contribution, 67 gauges, came from the Midlands Region where many records had been extended back into the 1970s by digitising charts. Thames Region provided data from 32 gauges and Anglian Region from 16 gauges, with the remaining data coming from the North East and Southern Regions. Most EA records are short, covering the 1980s and 1990s.

The *Scottish Environmental Protection Agency* provided 15 records of suitable length from recent years. These included some tables of hourly totals, from which annual maxima were abstracted manually. The gauges helped to fill large gaps in the network, particularly in the northern Highlands.

The *PEPR database* at IH holds rainfall data digitised from charts by a Precision Encoder and Pattern Recognition machine in a study involving the Greater London Council and the Met. Office (Moore *et al.*, 1993). PEPR data include some long records and extend up to 1976. These, and recent data from the Agency's Thames Region, added 27 gauges in Greater London and seven gauges elsewhere in England and Wales.

The *Department of Agriculture for Northern Ireland* (DANI) provided tables of hourly totals for eight gauges, which were computerised at IH. They cover the 1960s to the 1980s.

The DANI also arranged the provision of data from the *Irish Met. Service* for two gauges close to the N. Ireland border, both records spanning 1961 to 1990.

Recording raingauges installed by *IH* in experimental catchments added eight records, six of which are very close together at Plynlimon in mid-Wales. These data extend from the 1970s to the 1990s.

The total number of records received from recording raingauges is 567, including several pairs of records from different sources covering different periods at the same site. Figure 13.3 is a map of all recording raingauges providing at least nine annual maxima of 1-hour duration. The density of gauges is greatest in central England and Greater London. The largest gaps in the network are in western Scotland, the Grampian mountains, inland Devon and Cornwall, and North Wales. In some of these areas there are charts from tilting syphon recorders which have not been digitised. A search through catalogues of recording raingauges indicated that there have been tipping bucket recorders in some of these areas but it appears that some records have failed to survive organisational changes, and their location is not known.

13.3 Abstracting annual maxima

Annual maximum rainfalls were abstracted for calendar years, aggregating over durations 1, 2, 4, 6, 12, 18, and 24 hours and 1, 2, 4 and 8 days. The date and, for hourly data, the time of the start of each annual maximum were also recorded. Some gaps were identified but a year was discounted only if more than 25% of the data were missing. Very occasionally, a long-duration annual maximum may include one or more hours or days of missing data. Any such missing periods embedded in annual maxima were treated as zero rainfall depths.

The effect of including annual maxima from incomplete years was examined: a single-site sensitivity analysis showed that the effect was small. Most annual maximum series estimated from incomplete years are correct. At sites where the missing data do affect the annual maxima, the effects tend to compensate: a general underestimation in RMED is accompanied by a general overestimation of growth rates (Faulkner and Prudhomme, 1997).

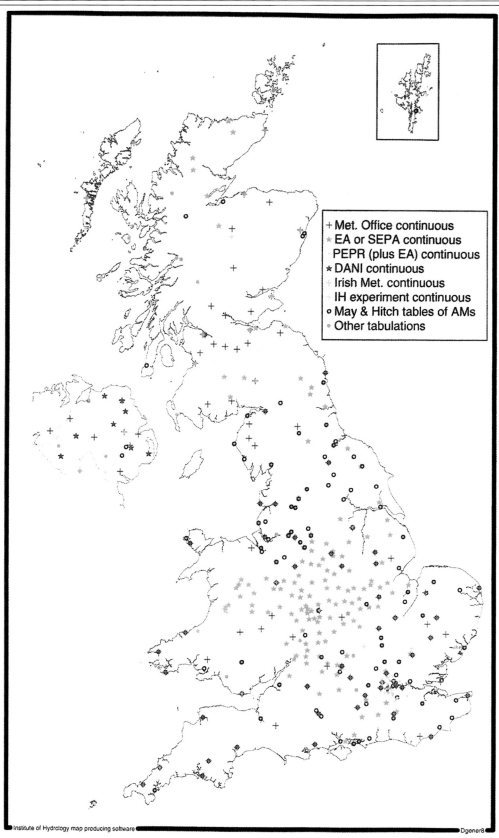

Figure 13.3   *Recording raingauges providing sufficient annual maxima*

For durations 2 to 24 hours and 2 to 8 days, care was taken at year-ends to ensure that every period of the required number of hours or days was covered by the abstraction algorithm. The convention used in each year was to include the last $D/2$ hours or days from the preceding year and the first $D/2$ from the following year, where D is the duration.

The May and Hitch (1989b) dataset contains 1-hour and 60-minute annual maximum values, together with their months of occurrence. The tabulated annual maxima which were computerised at IH cover durations including 2, 4, 6, 12 and 24 hours and 120 minutes. Rather more series are available for 1-hour rainfall than for longer durations. In most cases some date information was available, although generally only the month of occurrence of the maximum. Maxima relating to durations of 60 and 120 minutes were converted to equivalent 1 and 2 clock hour values by treating 60 and 120 minutes as sliding durations and using the conversion factors in Table 10.1.

13.4 Quality control

Errors in rainfall data can be introduced at several stages: at the raingauge, problems can be caused if the gauge is poorly sited or by flooding of the gauge, splashing of rainfall in or out, or losses due to hail, snow or high winds. Human error or technical failure is always possible, both in reading the gauge and in archiving the results. The quality control procedures aimed to identify and investigate suspicious annual maximum rainfalls.

13.4.1 Daily data

The daily data had already been subject to extensive quality control at the Met. Office. This was confirmed by searching the annual maximum database for the presence of suspiciously large or small values. A few large annual maxima were compared with nearby records, but only one change was made as a result: the 1 to 8-day maxima for 1963 at gauge 297785 were deleted.

One other change was made, undoing a change made by the Met. Office quality control procedure. Gauge 77255, Walshaw Dean Lodge, recorded the Calderdale storm on 19th May 1989. Hydrologists generally consider the recorded total of 193.2 mm to be valid (see Section 15.7), but the rainfall for the whole of May had been set to missing. The annual maxima for 1, 2, 4 and 8 days were set to 193.2 mm.

13.4.2 Hourly data

Annual maxima abstracted from continuous hourly data were checked against nearby daily totals. The hourly annual maxima were compared with totals for the three days surrounding the day on which the maximum was recorded, from the three nearest daily gauges.

Any suspiciously large hourly totals were investigated further by inspection of the continuous data from which the annual maximum was abstracted. These checks highlighted errors such as accumulations, where a large hourly total follows a period of missing data. Records from tipping bucket recorders (TBRs) sometimes showed large numbers of simultaneous tips. Some suspiciously large hourly totals were further investigated with more daily data and information from the British Rainfall yearbooks. After consultation with the suppliers of data, erroneous values were removed and the annual maxima re-abstracted. The total number of suspect annual maxima investigated was approximately 290.

Validation checks were not confined to looking for suspiciously high annual maxima. Annual maxima can be underestimated if a gauge is out of action for a significant period, or if it under-reads and is not scaled by totals from a daily check gauge. It was not always possible to distinguish dry periods from periods of missing record in TBR data. As a basic check, the depths recorded by TBRs for each year were accumulated to spot any years with long periods of missing data. It was thought possible that TBRs in the Hampshire area were under-reading, since they gave very low median annual maxima. The daily TBR totals were compared with check gauges, and in the end only one station required adjustment: Peel Common, gauge 323168.

Tabulated annual maxima and the May and Hitch dataset were crosschecked with each other and with annual maxima abstracted from continuous records, where they overlapped, to spot any inconsistencies. The previously abstracted annual maxima were held to be of good quality, and few errors were found.

Chapter 14 Summary of rainfall data

14.1 Summary statistics of the annual maximum database

Annual maximum rainfalls are held in two tables (hourly and daily) on the ORACLE database at IH. Some summary statistics of the database are given in Table 14.1. Note that these statistics refer only to gauges used in the analysis, i.e. those with sufficiently long records. The total number of station-years is compared with the approximate number used in the FSR rainfall analysis (reported by Stewart and Reynard, 1994). The increase in data quantity is striking for the 1-hour duration, where the number of station-years has more than trebled.

Table 14.1 Summary statistics of data used in the analysis

Duration	Number of gauges	Number of station-years	Approx. number of station-years used in FSR analysis
1 day	6106	150 245	96 000
1 hour	375	7389	2300

Figures 14.1 and 14.2 show the distributions of record length in the daily and hourly tables respectively. The difference in numbers of short-term and long-term daily gauges is reflected in Figure 14.1, which has a sharp drop in the number of series longer than 35-40 years. Short-term gauges — for which computerisation started in 1961 — had produced up to 36 annual maxima at the time of the analysis. Figure 14.2 reveals that most 1-hour series are short, with relatively few longer than 20 years. The longest records are around 100 years.

Dramatic growths and declines in the number of gauges providing data are illustrated by Figures 14.3 and 14.4, which show the number of 1-day and 1-hour annual maxima in the database for each year. Figure 14.3 reveals the relative sizes

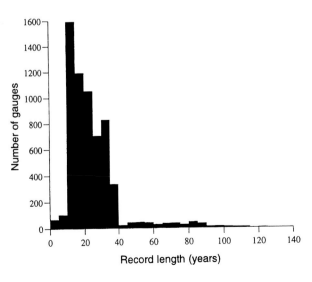

Figure 14.1   Distribution of record lengths of daily gauges

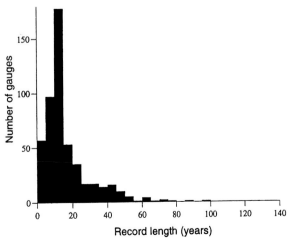

Figure 14.2   Distribution of record lengths of sub-daily gauges

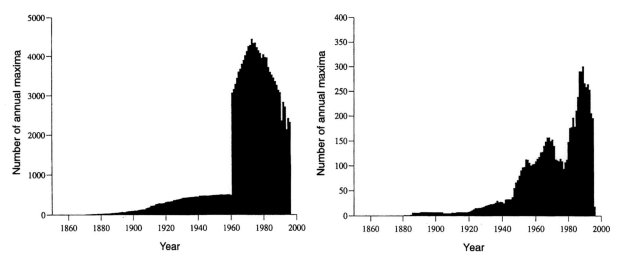

Figure 14.3   *Number of 1-day annual maxima for each year*   **Figure 14.4**   *Number of 1-hour annual maxima for each year*

of the long-term and short-term sets of daily rainfall data: in 1961 the number of annual maxima increases more than fivefold. There has been a steady decline in the number of daily gauges since 1970: many long-term gauges have been either discontinued or moved. Several influences are represented in Figure 14.4: there is a drop in the number of hourly annual maxima in the early 1970s when the FSR analysis was completed, then a substantial increase in the 1980s when tipping bucket recorders were installed widely.

14.2 Lists of raingauges

The recording raingauges used are listed in Appendix 1, which shows the site name, gauge number, grid reference and number of years of data. The number of daily gauges is too large for them to be listed in the FEH.

14.3 Trends in the data

While several studies have examined trend in flood frequency, weather types or monthly and annual total rainfalls, there has been little investigation of trend in UK rainfall extremes. Dales and Reed (1989) found no obvious trend in annual maximum 1-day rainfalls standardised by $SAAR_{4170}$. Their study was based on data from many gauges in England and Wales, extending from 1870 to 1980. Others have found shifts in the frequency of heavy 1-day rainfalls in some areas, for example Perry and Howells (1982) suggested that the frequency of heavy daily rainfall in south Wales has increased through this century.

An indication of any trends or fluctuations in the FEH rainfall dataset is given by Figures 14.5 and 14.6. Figure 14.5 shows the mean 1-day annual maximum rainfall at 38 gauges across the UK which operated from 1900 to 1990. There are a few gaps in some of the series, but most years have close to 38 annual maxima. There is a substantial year-to-year variation in the mean, but no evidence of an overall trend.

Figure 14.6 shows the 1-hour annual maximum rainfall averaged over all gauges, for all years with a significant number of operational gauges. It is not

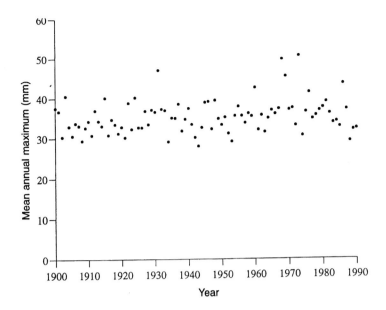

Figure 14.5 *Mean 1-day annual maximum for each year (38 gauges)*

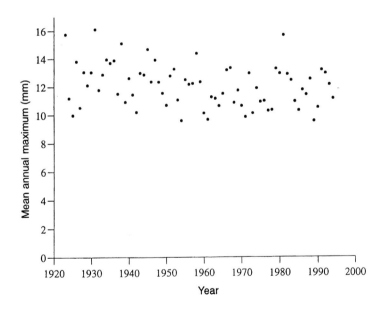

Figure 14.6 *Mean 1-hour annual maximum for each year (all UK gauges)*

possible to produce a 1-hour series from a fixed network of gauges because there are so few recording raingauges which have provided data for the whole period. At first sight there appears to be a slight downward trend in the mean, but this is unlikely to be significant, particularly in the light of changes in the type of raingauge and the geographical layout of the network.

Chapter 15 Recent noteworthy storms

15.1 Introduction

This chapter contains a selection of ten storms which have occurred in the UK between 1975 and 1998. They are all rare in terms of their rainfall total, and chosen to represent a range of locations, seasons and durations (and therefore a range of weather types). An earlier list, covering the years of the 20th century up to the writing of the FSR, is given in FSR Volume 2.

The description of each event includes a summary of the synoptic weather conditions which led up to the storm, a table of the greatest rainfall depths observed and their estimated return periods, and a description of the hydrological impacts of the rainfall. In most cases, there is also a map which shows rainfall accumulations at the site of raingauges, with no attempt at interpolation. The coastline and built-up areas are included. The scale of each map is indicated by the border, which shows National Grid references in units of km. In a few cases, the temporal profile of rainfall depths throughout the event is shown.

Where possible, the estimated rainfall rarities have been assessed from data spanning the period of the event only (i.e. hourly data for short events). In some cases where there are no hourly data, the duration of the event is known from the accounts of observers. If there was no other significant rainfall in the observing day, it can be assumed that the daily total fell within the period of the event only. In cases where this is not possible, return periods have been estimated by adjusting daily rainfall totals to account for discretisation, for example increasing 1-day rainfalls by a factor of 1.16 (from Table 2.1). Such adjustments are noted beside the estimated return period. The return period may be overestimated if in fact the 24-hour maximum rainfall coincided with the measurement day.

All times in the synoptic summaries are GMT. Return periods are rounded to avoid giving an impression of undue precision.

The information on the events is compiled from several sources: the weather logs accompanying the Royal Meteorological Society's *Weather* magazine; *Climatological Observers Link* (COL) bulletins; *Hydrological Data UK* yearbooks published by IH and BGS; predecessor yearbooks, *Surface Water UK,* published by the Water Data Unit; newspaper cuttings and letters from local staff of the gauging authorities. Other sources are specifically cited.

Rainfall totals come from the Met. Office, COL observers, the Environment Agency, journal articles and personal communications. The gauge number is the Met. Office reference number for a gauge at the site; in some cases this is inferred from the site name and may refer to another gauge at the same site. Not all sites have Met. Office reference numbers; in such cases, the number is replaced with the name of the organisation providing the data.

15.2 English Midlands and Wales, 9-10 April 1998

Synoptic summary

A depression moved south over the UK on 8th April, with a front bringing cold air and rain to catchments which were already wet. Another occluded front moved slowly north over southern England on 9th April, and there were thundery showers in the unstable air along the front. The two fronts reinforced each other, merging to create a slow-moving zone of intense and prolonged rainfall over central England and Wales (Bye and Horner, 1998).

Rainfall totals and rarities

Location (grid reference)	Gauge	Duration	Depth	Estimated return period
near Pershore (3973 2495)	457100	14 hr on 9th	76.6 mm	100 years
Great Malvern (3791 2470)	446802	14 hr on 9th	64.7 mm	50 years
near Church Lawford (4456 2736)	448621	11 hr on 9th	46.8 mm	11 years

Figure 15.2 is a map of the 2-day rainfall totals, which includes the raingauge locations, shown by open circles.

Evesham Journal. Used with permission.

Figure 15.1 *Stratford upon Avon town centre under water*

Hydrological impacts

The saturation of the ground and widespread intensity of the rain led to rivers rising at rates about twice as fast as previously experienced, to levels which were the highest on record at many locations (Bye and Horner, 1998). Sudden and severe flooding over a wide area included Stratford upon Avon, Leamington Spa, Northampton, Kidlington, Skenfrith and Evesham. Around 4500 properties flooded and five people died. Several villages were cut off and there was a 40-mile traffic jam on the M40.

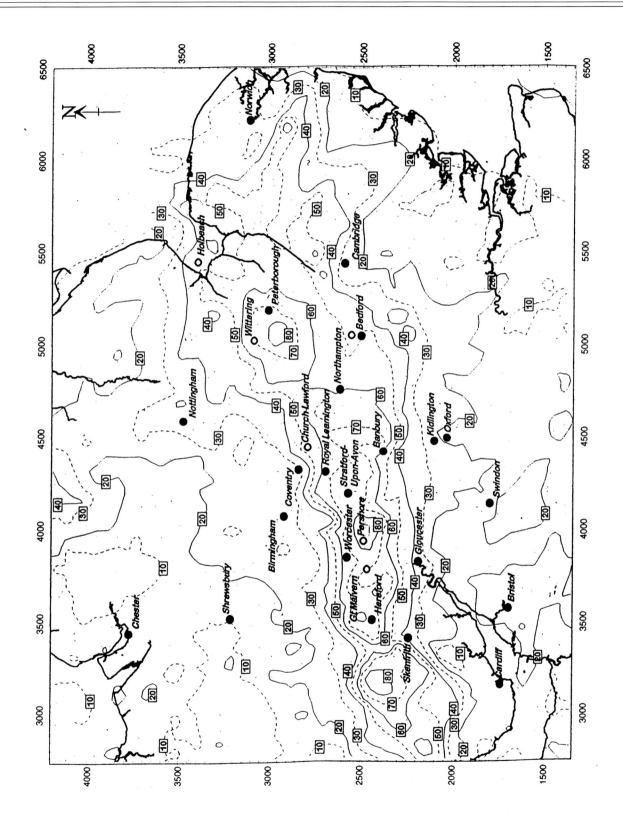

Figure 15.2 *Contoured 2-day rainfall totals in mm for 9-10 April, with locations and raingauges. Based on Bye and Horner (1998), using Met. Office data.*

15.3 Sconser, Isle of Skye, 6-28 February 1997

Synoptic summary

The mean air pressure for February 1997 over the Western Isles was some 17 mbar below normal, as an almost unbroken succession of active Atlantic disturbances affected the British Isles. North-west Britain was exceptionally wet, particularly in mountainous areas such as Skye, where there was strong orographic enhancement of rainfall. The temperature was consistently mild and there were frequent gales. At Sconser, winds gusted from severe gale to storm force every day from 16th to the end of February.

Rainfall totals and rarities

Location (grid reference)	Gauge	Duration	Depth	Estimated return period
Sconser (1510 8310)	COL	9 days (17-25th)	562 mm	12000 years
		24 days (6.2-1.3)	1078 mm	n/a
Broadford (1652 8230)	721604	9 days	170 mm	1 year
Glen Dessary (1968 7926)	692783	9 days	314 mm	3 years

Without a thorough investigation, it is difficult to comment on such extreme and diverging rainfalls and rarities. The difference between the 9-day rainfalls observed at Sconser and Broadford, only 16 km away, is remarkable, but Sconser is strongly influenced by orographic enhancement over the Cuillin mountains to the southwest.

Even if the rainfall at Sconser is correct, the return period of 12000 years is probably overestimated: RMED at Sconser is poorly estimated because there are few sample values from the Sconser area, or anywhere in the Cuillins. The immense difference between the estimated return periods at Sconser and Broadford is a combination of the difference in rainfall and the likely overestimation of the return period at Sconser. Although some of the figures may be unreliable, they are a reminder of the extreme local rainfall variations in mountainous areas.

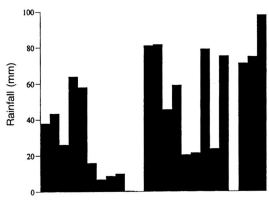

Figure 15.3 *Daily rainfall at Sconser, 6th February – 1st March 1997*

Hydrological impacts

Despite the exceptional sequence of very wet days, there was no flooding of property in Sconser during the month. However, flooding of many roads was reported in mainland Scotland.

15.4 Glasgow, 8-12 December 1994

Synoptic summary

Bands of showers moved across Glasgow from the northwest, followed early on the 10th by a warm front from the west. This introduced a very mild and moist southwesterly airflow which persisted for two days and brought prolific rainfall in the "conveyor belt" ahead of a slow-moving cold front. The rain finally died out in the early hours of the 12th, when the cold front crossed the area (Faulkner, 1997).

Rainfall totals and rarities

Location (grid reference)	Gauge	Duration	Depth	Estimated return period
Kaim Dam (2346 6622)	659231	5 days	258 mm	200 years
Gleniffer Braes (2435 6595)	659594	5 days	258 mm	600 years
Castle Semple Loch (2364 6594)	659409	5 days	233 mm	100 years
Neilston Filters (2475 6564)	660928	5 days	233 mm	220 years

Extreme rainfall totals covered a wide area. The return period of a given depth varies widely because of the variable topography around Glasgow.

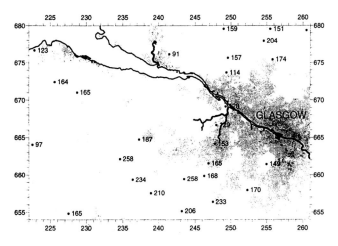

Figure 15.4 Rainfall (mm) on 8-12 Dec 1994 around Glasgow

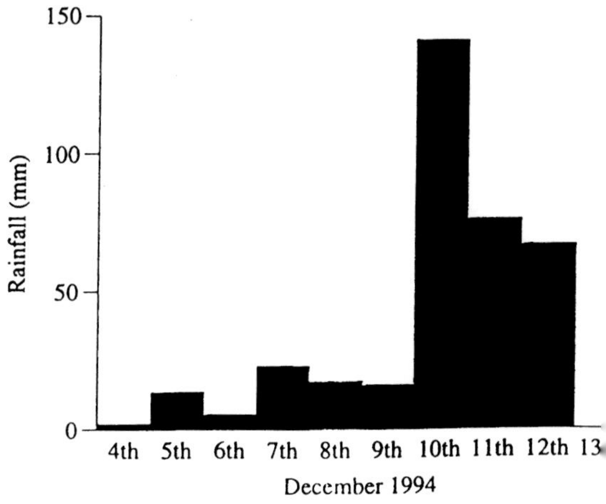

Figure 15.5 Daily rainfall at Kaim Dam

Hydrological impacts

Nearly 700 homes were flooded in Kirkintilloch and Paisley. Bridges were destroyed and three people were drowned (Alexander Howden, 1995). A low-level railway tunnel was out of action for a year afterwards.

15.5 Ditchingham, Norfolk, 31 August -1 September 1994, 21:00-08:00.

Synoptic summary

A depression moved from northern France over south-east England to the North Sea, with embedded thunderstorms producing localised downpours, including one at Ditchingham.

Rainfall totals and rarities

Location (grid reference)	Gauge	Duration	Depth	Estimated return period
Ditchingham (6340 2906)	211668	1 day	144 mm	
" (assuming all rain fell in 12 h)	211668	12 hours	144 mm	1000 years
Ditchingham (6330 2917)	211896	1 day	147 mm	
Barsham (6406 2896)	212059	1 day	114 mm	
Woodton (6295 2954)	211831	1 day	121 mm	
Framingham (6272 3030)	NRA	6 hours	83 mm	240 years

The rainfall of 147 mm in one day was the highest observed daily total in south-east Britain since the 1975 Hampstead storm (see Section 15.10)

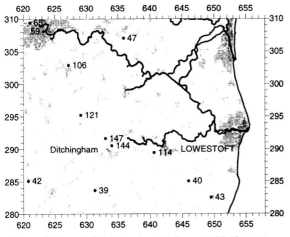

Figure 15.6 Rainfall (mm) on 31 August 1994 in east Norfolk

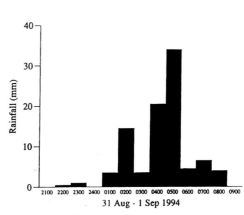

Figure 15.7 Hourly rainfall at Framingham

Hydrological impacts

A wall in a school was destroyed and school buildings flooded. Some properties were flooded in Beccles, including the hospital.

15.6 Upton Scudamore, Wiltshire, 17-18 September 1992, mainly 06:00 to 16:00 on 18th

Synoptic summary

An anticyclone developed over Britain on the 16th September; on the 17th humid south-easterlies brought thundery showers. In the early hours of the 18th violent storms moved across England from the southwest, with further storms in the afternoon.

Rainfall totals and rarities

Location (grid reference)	Gauge	Duration	Depth	Estimated return period
Upton Scudamore (3860 1480)	unknown	10 hours	96 mm	200 years
Upton Scudamore (3864 1483)	413479	2 days	111 mm	

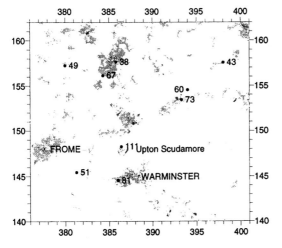

Figure 15.8 Rainfall (mm) on 17-18 Sept. 1992 around Upton Scudamore

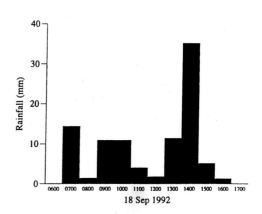

Figure 15.9 Hourly rainfall at Upton Scudamore

Hydrological impacts

Flash floods occurred, for example at Dilton Marsh and Warminster. There was also much damage by lightning.

15.6 Calderdale, West Yorkshire, 19 May 1989, 15:00-17:00

Synoptic summary

An anticyclone lay over the northern North Sea, the remains of a front close to Scottish borders, with very warm and humid air to the south. The event was a torrential, localised thunderstorm, with a small amount of hail (Acreman, 1989).

Rainfall totals and rarities

Location (grid reference)	Gauge	Duration	Depth	Estimated return period
Walshaw Dean Lodge (3964 4336)	77255	2 hours	193 mm	6000 years

The rainfall total is controversial: the Met. Office conceded only that the depth was at least 40 mm (Met. Office, 1990; Collier, 1991). However, the depth of 193 mm has been thoroughly investigated (Acreman and Collinge 1991), and it represents the largest 2-hour total observed in the UK.

Evening Courier, Halifax. Used with permission.

Figure 15.10 *Luddenden village during the flood*

Hydrological impacts

Many properties were flooded in Halifax, with erosion and severe damage to river retaining walls, mill foundations, culverts and sewers. A landslide was caused by a peat bog bursting below Walshaw Dean Lodge. Cars and garden sheds were swept away and houses flooded to a depth of a metre in Luddenden (Acreman and Collinge, 1991).

15.8 South Wales, 26-27 December 1979

Synoptic summary

Fronts moving from the west associated with low pressure systems to the north of Scotland brought prolonged rain and gales over all of the UK apart from northern Scotland. Most of the rain in south Wales was due to a slow-moving cold front (Browning, 1980).

Rainfall totals and rarities

Location (grid reference)	Gauge	Duration	Depth	Estimated return period
Aberdare (2998 2021)	489901	20 hours	150 mm	30 years
Treorchy (2968 1964)	490295	22 hours	137 mm	16 years

The rainfall return periods are discussed by Jack (1981).

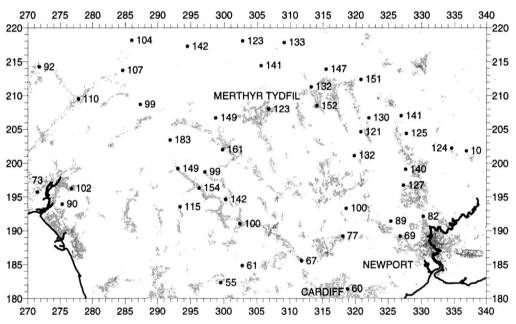

Figure 15.11 Rainfall (mm) on 26-27 December 1979 in south Wales

Hydrological impacts

In widespread flooding, four people were drowned, thousands evacuated and hundreds of homes flooded in Merthyr Tydfil, Brecon, Cardiff and elsewhere (Thomas, 1980; DOE, 1995).

15.9 Middlesex and Buckinghamshire, 16-17 August 1977, overnight

Synoptic summary

A low pressure area over northern France was moving northeast on 16th August, giving a east-southeast airstream over southeast England. After a warm humid day, rain accompanied by thunder moved across the English Channel from the southeast. Widespread continuous thunderstorms reached southeast England and London by late evening. The weather continued to be extraordinarily wet for the next 8 days (COL, 1997).

Rainfall totals and rarities

Location (grid reference)	Gauge	Duration (assumed)	Depth	Estimated return period
Chalfont St. Peter (5004 1925)	279314	12 hours	115 mm	300 years
Ruislip (5090 1880)	COL	12 hours	113 mm	400 years
Maple Lodge (5037 1922)	278932	12 hours	113 mm	300 years
Ickenham (5074 1875)	279544	12 hours	110 mm	350 years

The rainfall totals were accumulated over one measurement day, but most of the rainfall is believed to have fallen in 12 hours, overnight.

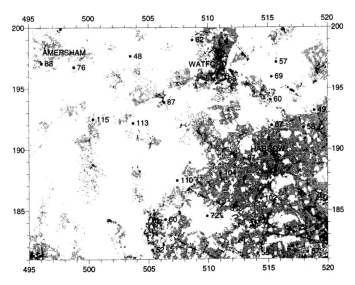

Figure 15.12 Rainfall (mm) on 16 August 1977 in northwest London

Hydrological impacts

There was widespread flooding of houses, stations and roads.

15.10 Hampstead, north London, 14 August 1975, 16:00-19:00

Synoptic summary

14th August marked the end of a three-week heatwave in southern Britain. The warm air (29-31°C in places) was gradually displaced as a cold front advanced from the west. The Hampstead event was an isolated and extremely severe thunderstorm which remained stationary for about 2 hours and 40 minutes. It is possible that the hill of Hampstead Heath served as a local focus for the development of the storm. There was some hail towards the end of the storm (Meaden, 1975; Tyssen-Gee, 1981).

Rainfall totals and rarities

Location (grid reference)	Gauge	Duration (assumed)	Depth	Estimated return period
Hampstead Obs. (5262 1863)	246690	3 hours	171 mm	1800 years
Golders Hill Park (5256 1870)	246692	3 hours	131 mm	800 years
Crouch End, Priory Park (5300 1891)	245166	3 hours	74 mm	130 years

The rainfall totals were accumulated over 1 day, but observers confirmed that there was only 1-2 mm of light rain outside the 3-hour-long thunderstorm.

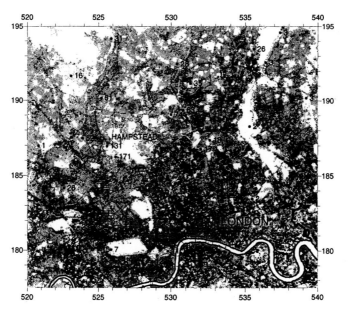

Figure 15.13   Rainfall (mm) on 14 August 1975 in north London

Hydrological impacts

This was a severe flood: cars floated along streets, houses were damaged, subways filled, sewers burst. Two people drowned in basements; two were struck by lightning.

15.11 Loch Sloy, Strathclyde Region, 17-18 January 1974

Synoptic summary

Strong southerly and south-westerly winds brought fronts, associated with a large area of low pressure around Iceland, to Scotland. A broad warm sector moved over Scotland on 17th-18th, giving Scotland's highest ever daily rainfall at Loch Sloy.

Rainfall totals and rarities

Location (grid reference)	Gauge	Duration (adj. to 24 hour)	Depth	Estimated return period
Sloy Main Adit (2293 7104)	662119	1 day	238 mm	750 years
"	662119	2 days	300 mm	450 years
Sloy Power Station (2321 7098)	662042	1 day	138 mm	40 years

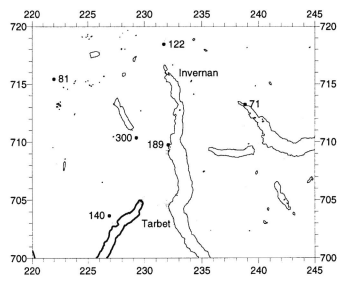

Figure 15.14   *Rainfall (mm) on 17-18 January 1974 around Loch Sloy. Loch Lomond and other freshwater lochs are marked by thin lines.*

Hydrological impacts

There is no record of any impacts in the yearbooks and weather logs consulted.

Acknowledgements

This volume arose from a rainfall frequency study in England and Wales, commissioned by the Environment Agency (EA). It is equivalent to EA Technical Report W184 produced by R&D project number W5A-044. Thanks are due to the Agency's project leader, Linda Aucott, who also coordinated the gathering of information on sub-daily rainfall data from the EA regions. The extension of the work to Scotland and Northern Ireland was funded by a consortium, led by the Scottish Office and the Rivers Agency of the Department of Agriculture for Northern Ireland (DANI).

The research for this volume was made possible by certain memoranda of understanding with the Met. Office, one of which was a tripartite agreement between IH, the Met. Office and the Environment Agency. The memoranda gave the FEH team access to additional datasets of daily and sub-daily rainfall measurements.

Rainfall data were provided by the Met. Office, the Environment Agency, the Scottish Environment Protection Agency (SEPA), DANI, the Irish Met. Service, the Institute of Hydrology and the Climatological Observers Link. The work of the staff of these organisations is gratefully acknowledged, together with their patience in dealing with quality control enquiries. In particular, Andrew Pimperton of the Environment Agency Midlands Region and Philip Procter and Ann Ruane of the EA Yorkshire Area spent much time arranging the digitising of rainfall charts. Viv Turner of the Agency's Northumbria Area is thanked for undertaking the difficult task of gathering and checking data in several different formats. The coverage of Northern Ireland was greatly enhanced through the efforts of John Clarke, Stephen Dawson and Derrick Pinkerton at DANI. Extensive tabulated hourly rainfalls provided by DANI were patiently computerised at IH by Victoria Edmunds and Miranda Gibbs. Brian May of the Met. Office gave permission to use the May and Hitch dataset; these and the continuous data were supplied by George Anderson and Paul Harker.

The development of the FORGEX method was guided by Duncan Reed and Lisa Stewart. David Jones is thanked for suggesting the bootstrapping method (Chapter 9) and the network maximum plotting positions (Chapter 8).

References

Acreman, M.C. 1989. Extreme rainfall in Calderdale, 19 May 1989. *Weather* **44**, 438-446.

Acreman, M.C. and Collinge, V.K. 1991. The Calderdale storm revisited: an assessment of the evidence. In: Proc. Third National Hydrology Symposium, Southampton 1991, British Hydrological Society, 4.11-4.16.

Adby, P.R. and Dempster, M.A.H. 1974. *Introduction to Optimization Methods*, Chapman and Hall, London.

Alexander Howden 1995. Flooding in Glasgow and Ayrshire. Alexander Howden Group, London.

Bell, F.C. 1976. The areal reduction factor in rainfall frequency estimation. *IH Report No. 35*, Institute of Hydrology, Wallingford.

Bilham, E.G. 1935. Classification of heavy falls of rain in short periods. *British Rainfall 1935*, 262-280. HMSO, London.

Bootman, A.P. and Willis, A. 1981. Discussion of paper 5 (Folland *et al.*), In: *Flood Studies Report – five years on*, Institution of Civil Engineers, London, 62-63.

Browning, K.A. 1980. The south Wales floods of late December 1979. *Weather* **35**, 202-203.

Buishand, T.A. 1991. Extreme rainfall estimation by combining data from several sites. *Hydrol. Sci. J.* **36**, 345-365.

Buishand, T.A. 1993. Rainfall Depth-Duration-Frequency Curves; a Problem of Dependent Extremes. In: Barnett, V. and Turkman, K.F. (eds) *Statistics for the Environment*, John Wiley & Sons, 183-197.

Butters, K. 1975. In: Discussion on papers 1 and 2, *Flood Studies Conference*, Institution of Civil Engineers, London, 11-21.

Butters, K. and Vairavamoorthy, A. 1977. Hydrological studies on some river catchments in Greater London. *Proc. ICE*, Pt 2, **63**, 331-361.

Bye, P. and Horner, M. 1998. *Easter 1998 Floods*. Report by the Independent Review Team to the Board of the Environment Agency. Two volumes.

Chandler, T.J. and Gregory, S. (Eds) 1976. *The Climate of the British Isles*. Longman, London.

Chen, C. 1983. Rainfall intensity-duration-frequency formulas. *J. Hydraul. Engin., ASCE* **109**, 1603-1621.

Clark, C. 1997. How rare is that storm in southwest England? *Meteorol. Appl.* **5**, 139-148.

CCIRG 1996. Review of the potential impacts of climate change in the UK. Climate Change Impacts Review Group. Department of the Environment, The Stationery Office, London.

COL 1997. *COL Bulletin*, August 1997. Climatological Observers Link.

Collier, C.G. 1991. Problems of estimating extreme rainfall from radar and raingauge data illustrated by the Halifax storm, 19 May 1989. *Weather* **46**, 200-209.

Dales, M.Y. and Reed, D.W. 1989. Regional flood and storm hazard assessment. *IH Report No. 102*, Institute of Hydrology, Wallingford.

DOE 1981. Design and analysis of urban storm drainage. The Wallingford procedure. Volume 1. National Water Council, London. Department of the Environment

DOE 1995. The occurrence and significance of erosion, deposition and flooding in Great Britain. Department of the Environment. HMSO, London.

Dwyer, I.J. and Reed, D.W. 1995. Allowance for discretization in hydrological and environmental risk estimation (ADHERE). *IH Report No. 123*, Institute of Hydrology, Wallingford.

Efron, B. 1979. Bootstrap methods: another look at the jack-knife. *Annals of Statistics*, **7**, 1-26.

Faiers, G.E., Keim, B.D. and Hirschboeck, K.K. 1994. A synoptic evaluation of frequencies and intensities of extreme three and 24-hour rainfall in Louisiana. *Professional Geographer* **46**, 156-163.

Faulkner, D.S. 1997. Characteristics of recent UK flood-producing rainfalls in relation to the Flood Studies Report design event method. *Met. Appl.* **4**, 259-268.

Faulkner, D.S. 1998. Design rainfalls for urban drainage: the Flood Estimation Handbook. *Proc. Wastewater Planning Users Group (WAPUG) Autumn Meeting,* Blackpool.

Faulkner, D.S. and Jones, D.A. 1999. The FORGEX method of rainfall frequency estimation III: Performance. *Hydrol. and Earth System Sci.,* in press.

Faulkner, D.S. and Prudhomme, C. 1997. Rainfall Frequency Estimation in England and Wales. Phase 2: Production. R&D Draft Technical Report, Environment Agency, Bristol.

Faulkner, D.S. and Prudhomme, C. 1998. Mapping an index of extreme rainfall across the UK. *Hydrol. and Earth System Sci.* **2**, 183-194.

Ferreri, G.B. and Ferro, V. 1990. Short-duration rainfalls in Sicily, *J. Hydraul. Engin., ASCE* **116**, 430-435.

Garside, I.G. 1991. Using annual rainfall time series. WAPUG User Note No. 23.

Gregory, J.M. and Mitchell, J.F.B. 1995. Simulation of daily variability of surface temperature and precipitation over Europe in the current and $2 \times CO_2$ climates using the UKMO model. *Quart. J. R. Met. Soc.* **121**, 1451-1476.

Holland, D.J. 1968. Rain intensity frequency relationships in Britain. *Hydrological Memoranda No. 33.* Met. Office.

Hosking, J.R.M. and Wallis, J.R. 1988. The Effect of Intersite Dependence on Regional Flood Frequency Analysis. *Water Resour. Res.* **24**, 588-600.

Hosking, J.R.M. and Wallis, J.R. 1997. *Regional Frequency Analysis: An Approach Based on L-Moments.* Cambridge University Press.

Institute of Engineers, Australia 1987. Australian Rainfall and Runoff.

IH 1977. The estimation of low return period floods. *Flood Studies Supplementary Report No. 2,* Institute of Hydrology, Wallingford.

Institution of Civil Engineers 1996. *Floods and Reservoir Safety: An Engineering Guide,* 3rd edn, Thomas Telford, London.

IPCC 1996. *The science of climate change.* Houghton, J.T., Meira-Filho, L.G., Callander, B.A., Harris, N., Kattenburg, A. and Maskell, K. (eds). Intergovernmental Panel on Climate Change. Cambridge University Press.

Jack, W.L. 1981. Rainfall return periods for December 1979. *Weather* **36**, 274-276.

Johnson, F.G., Jarvis, R.M. and Reynolds, G. 1981. Use made of the Flood Studies Report for reservoir operation in hydroelectric schemes. In: *Flood Studies Report – five years on,* Institution of Civil Engineers, London. 85-90.

Jones, D.A. 1997. Plotting positions via maximum-likelihood for some non-standard situations. *Hydrol. and Earth System Sci.* **1**, 357-366.

Journel, A.G. and Huijbregts C.J. 1978. *Mining geostatistics.* Academic Press, London.

Keers, J.F. and Wescott, P. 1977. A computer-based model for design rainfall in the United Kingdom. *Met. Office Scientific Paper No. 36.* HMSO, London.

Kelway, P.S. 1975. In: Discussion on papers 1 and 2, *Flood Studies Conference,* Institution of Civil Engineers, London, 11-21.

Konrad, C. 1996. Relationships between precipitation event types and topography in the southern Blue Ridge mountains of the southeastern USA. *Int. J. Climatol.* **16**, 49-62.

Martin, R. 1975. In: Discussion on papers 1 and 2, *Flood Studies Conference,* Institution of Civil Engineers, London, 11-21.

May, B.R. and Hitch, T.J. 1989a. Periodic fluctuations in extreme hourly rainfalls in the United Kingdom. *Met. Mag.* **118**, 45-50.

May, B.R. and Hitch, T.J. 1989b. Improved values of 1-hour M5 rainfalls for the United Kingdom. *Met. Mag.* **118**, 76-81.

Meaden, G.T. (ed.) 1975. The Hampstead deluge of 14 August 1975. *J. Met.* **1**, 6-8.

Metcalfe, A.V. 1994. *Statistics in engineering.* Chapman and Hall, London.

Met. Office 1990. Addendum to *British Rainfall 1989.* Meteorological Office, UK.

Moore, R.J., Hotchkiss, D.S. and Black, K.B. 1993) *Rainfall patterns over London.* Report to NRA Thames Region. Institute of Hydrology, Wallingford.

Nandakumar, N., Weinmann, P.E., Mein, R.G. and Nathan, R.J. 1997. Estimation of extreme rainfalls for Victoria using the CRC-FORGE method. *Report 97/4,*

Cooperative Research Centre for Catchment Hydrology, Australia.

Onof, C., Faulkner, D.S. and Wheater, H.S. 1996. Design rainfall modelling in the Thames catchment. *Hydrol. Sci. J.* **41**, 715-733.

Perry, A.H. and Howells, K.A. 1982. Are large falls of rain in Wales becoming more frequent? *Weather* **37**, 240-243.

Phillips, D.L., Dolph, J. and Marks, D. 1992. A comparison of geostatistical procedures for spatial analysis of precipitation in mountainous terrain. *Agric. For. Met.* **58,** 119-141.

Pilgrim, D.H., Cordery, I. and French, R. 1969. Temporal patterns of design rainfall for Sydney. *Civ. Eng. Trans. I.E. Aust.* **CE11**, 9-14.

Prudhomme, C. and Reed, D.W. 1998. Relationships between extreme daily precipitation and topography in a mountainous region: a case study in Scotland. *Intl. J. Climatol.* **18**, 1439-1453.

Reed, D.W., Faulkner, D.S. and Stewart, E.J. 1999. The FORGEX method of rainfall growth estimation II: Description. *Hydrol. and Earth System Sci.*, in press.

Reed, D.W. and Stewart, E.J. 1989. Focus on rainfall growth estimation. In: Proc. Second National Hydrology Symposium, Sheffield, British Hydrological Society, 3.57-3.65.

Reed, D.W. and Stewart, E.J. 1994. Inter-site and inter-duration dependence in rainfall extremes. In: Barnett, V. and Turkman, K.F. (eds) *Statistics for the Environment 2: water-related issues,* John Wiley & Sons, 125-143.

Reynard, N.S. and Stewart, E.J. 1993. The derivation of design rainfall profiles for upland areas of the United Kingdom. *Met. Mag.* **122,** 116-123.

Reynolds, G. 1975. In: Discussion on papers 1 and 2, *Flood Studies Conference,* Institution of Civil Engineers, London, 11-21.

Shaw, E.M. 1994. *Hydrology in Practice.* 3rd edn, Chapman and Hall, London.

Stewart, E.J. 1989. Areal reduction factors for design storm construction: Joint use of radar and raingauge data. In: New Directions for Surface Water Modelling. *IAHS Publ. No. 181,* Internat. Assoc. of Hydrological Sciences Press, Wallingford. 31-40.

Stewart, E.J., Faulkner, D.S. and Reynard, N.S. 1995. Rainfall Frequency Estimation in England and Wales. Phase 1b: Pilot Study. R&D Note 478, National Rivers Authority, Bristol.

Stewart, E.J., Reed, D.W., Faulkner, D.S. and Reynard, N.S. 1999. The FORGEX method of rainfall frequency estimation I: Requirement. *Hydrol. and Earth System Sci.,* in press.

Stewart, E.J. and Reynard, N.S. 1991. Rainfall profiles for design events of long duration. In: Proc. Third National Hydrology Symposium, Southampton, British Hydrological Society, 4.27-4.36.

Stewart, E.J. and Reynard, N.S. 1994. Rainfall Frequency Estimation in England and Wales. Phase 1a: Survey. R&D Note 175, National Rivers Authority, Bristol.

Tabony, R.C. 1983. Extreme value analysis in meteorology. *Met. Mag.* **112**, 1329, 77-98.

Thielen, J. and Gadian, A. 1997. Influence of topography and urban heat island effects on the outbreak of convective storms under unstable meteorological conditions: a numerical study. *Met. Appl.* **4**, 139-149.

Thomas, A.J. 1980. Deaths in Britain from the weather during 1979. *J. Met.* **5**, 154-155.

Tyssen-Gee, R.A. 1981. Hampstead's 70 years of rainfall figures. *J. Met.* **6**, 3-8.

Vairavamoorthy, A., Rylands, W.D. and Mills, D.N. 1990. FRQSIM – a flood hydrology model. In: White, W.R. (ed.) *International Conference on River Flood Hydraulics,* John Wiley & Sons, 41-51.

Appendix 1   List of recording raingauges

This list includes all recording raingauges with at least nine annual maximum 1-hour rainfalls in the FEH database. The list is broken down by region. Note that some gauge numbers are not standard Met. Office numbers, for example some Environment Agency gauges in the Midlands and Anglian regions, which do not have Met. Office numbers, have been allocated 7-figure numbers starting in 9. Not all years in the range necessarily have valid annual maxima.

Gauge number	Site	Easting	Northing	First year	Last year
North-east England					
1584	Boulmer Met.Office	4253	6142	1975	1995
3066	Linbriggs Logger Sta.	3892	6062	1982	1995
5193	Acklington Met.Office	4225	6007	1947	1974
5782	Wallington Logger Sta.	4035	5843	1983	1995
6403	Font Resr P.Sta. Logger Sta.	4052	5938	1982	1995
19356	Jesmond Dene Logger Sta.	4253	5672	1984	1995
21228	Burnhope Resr SSER	3850	5391	1981	1995
24724	Durham	4267	5415	1946	1959
27035	Forest-in-Teesdale	3872	5295	1951	1970
28185	Lartington Filters Logger Sta.	4011	5183	1982	1995
31451	Middleton St George, Met Office	4376	5132	1952	1963
31555	Easby Logger Sta.	4584	5087	1982	1995
32602	Hartburn Grange	4407	5185	1959	1986
42667	Driffield Met.Office	5004	4565	1948	1958
44228	Leconfield Met.Office	5026	4438	1960	1968
44704	Cottingham P.Sta. Logger Sta.	5048	4342	1988	1996
44877	Hull, Ringrose St	5067	4281	1963	1973
52787	Catterick Met.Office	4249	4970	1932	1944
53904	Leeming	4306	4890	1945	1995
56316	Dishforth Met.Office	4379	4723	1951	1964
58569	Harrogate	4304	4578	1952	1971
60528	York, Heslington	4631	4512	1967	1979
64421	Church Fenton	4528	4380	1947	1989
68782	Farndale Vicarage	4673	4975	1935	1971
70676	Pickering	4795	4843	1974	1996
74374	Skipton Town Hall	3991	4518	1913	1970
83280	Wingerworth Logger Sta.	4378	3665	1986	1996
86575	South Elmsall S.Wks Logger Sta.	4484	4107	1985	1996
Trent and Severn catchments (English and Welsh midlands)					
89542	Keele	3820	3446	1952	1995
90803	Stone, Cold Norton Farm	3878	3321	1986	1995
91267	Barnhurst W.Recl.Wks	3901	3017	1983	1995
91860	Hollies P.Sta. Auto Sta.	3816	3224	1982	1995
93536	Blithfield Resr	4071	3226	1975	1995
95802	Minworth S.Wks Auto.Sta.	4164	2922	1976	1992
96893	Elmdon	4167	2841	1949	1992

Gauge number	Site	Easting	Northing	First year	Last year
98210	Hinckley S.Wks	4420	2927	1963	1995
99321	Atherstone S. Wks. Auto Sta.	4318	2980	1984	1995
100449	Overseal S.Wks	4291	3149	1974	1995
101151	Claymills W.Recl.Wks	4265	3259	1984	1995
101204	Hollinsclough Auto Sta.	4066	3665	1986	1995
102367	Ashbourne, St Oswald's Hospital Auto.Sta	4173	3465	1985	1995
103072	Stanley Resr Auto Sta.	3929	3519	1981	1995
107268	Barbrook Resr	4281	3770	1982	1995
108786	Longcliffe Resr Auto Sta.	4228	3553	1982	1995
109084	Ashover	4349	3629	1970	1993
109141	Ogston Resr	4380	3598	1964	1995
111398	Narborough S.Wks	4549	2966	1971	1995
113774	Brooksby Hall	4679	3154	1981	1995
115296	Mount St Bernard Abbey Auto.Sta.	4459	3158	1986	1995
117626	Nottingham Weather Centre	4503	3456	1948	1993
122707	Sutton-in-Ashfield S.Wks	4510	3595	1986	1995
125842	Finningley	4659	3989	1951	1993
125843	Finningley Met.Office	4658	3995	1951	1970
421140	Dolydd	2873	2905	1980	1995
423198	Cefn Coch P. Sta. Auto.Sta.	3042	3026	1983	1995
423601	Sarn S.Wks Auto.Sta.	3206	2906	1981	1995
424216	Welshpool S.Wks	3233	3073	1980	1995
425001	Lake Vyrnwy	3017	3188	1985	1995
425646	Pen-y-Coed Auto.Sta.	2978	3144	1982	1995
426593	Llanfyllin W.Recl.Wks	3154	3188	1980	1995
426853	Llangynog W.Recl.Wks	3053	3259	1982	1995
429082	Bagley Auto.Sta.	3413	3277	1983	1995
430296	Shrewsbury, Monkmoor S.Wks Auto.Sta.	3517	3136	1985	1995
431324	Child's Ercall S.Wks	3663	3249	1985	1995
432811	Rushmoor W.Recl.Wks	3617	3135	1985	1995
433710	Shawbury Met.Office	3553	3220	1975	1993
435507	Cosford W.Wks No.2	3782	3047	1983	1995
437138	Trimpley W.Wks	3772	2789	1985	1995
437694	Lye W.Recl.Wks	3919	2849	1982	1995
438925	Hartlebury Auto.Sta.	3846	2698	1979	1995
441009	Bettws-y-Crwyn Auto.Sta.	3203	2814	1982	1995
443093	Craven Arms S.Wks	3437	2811	1980	1995
443216	Oakly Park	3491	2762	1980	1990
444887	Ditton Priors No.2 Auto.Sta.	3604	2882	1979	1995
446802	Great Malvern	3791	2470	1986	1995
446964	Malvern Met.Office	3787	2447	1977	1985
447787	Stanford Resr	4596	2804	1964	1995
448545	Rugby	4507	2749	1980	1993
449958	Finham W.Recl.Wks	4334	2740	1983	1995
450777	Knightcote Farm Auto.Sta.	4398	2545	1979	1995
453096	Chipping Campden, W.Recl.Wks	4164	2393	1981	1995
453420	Shipston on Stour, W.Recl.Wks	4268	2411	1980	1995
453925	Milcote W.Recl.Wks	4182	2528	1979	1995

Gauge number	Site	Easting	Northing	First year	Last year
454433	Lye Bridge W.Recl.Wks	4032	2717	1982	1995
457100	Pershore Met.Office	3973	2495	1958	1976
457597	Crowle W.Recl.Wks Auto.Sta.	3934	2558	1981	1995
457944	Defford Met.Office	3899	2422	1949	1957
458845	Dowdeswell Resr No.2	3983	2198	1979	1995
459426	Longford W.Recl.Wks Auto.Sta.	3847	2209	1980	1995
459794	Ledbury W.Recl.Wks	3702	2371	1981	1995
461468	Miserden	3937	2087	1982	1995
9000001	Henley-in-Arden	4154	2679	1981	1995
9000009	Braunston	4533	2658	1982	1995
9000010	Rodbaston	3920	3116	1986	1995
9000019	Frankley	4007	2801	1986	1995
9000021	Warley Park	4010	2861	1965	1988
9000030	Walsall Wood	4038	3042	1983	1995
9000039	Kirk Langley	4293	3392	1981	1992
9000041	Spondon	4395	3345	1986	1995
9000047	Wanlip	4598	3117	1986	1995
9000048	Fleckney	4656	2946	1986	1995
9000049	Whissendine	4829	3144	1986	1995
9000050	Colwick	4615	3393	1986	1995
9000054	Worksop	4608	3791	1983	1995

Anglian region

Gauge number	Site	Easting	Northing	First year	Last year
136580	Manby Met.Office	5393	3867	1952	1970
141160	Upton S.Wks Auto.Sta.	4877	3868	1978	1993
142001	Waddington Met.Office	4988	3653	1947	1993
146127	Coningsby Met.Office	5224	3568	1982	1993
146451	Cranwell Met.Office	5004	3493	1922	1993
146966	Guthram Gowt Auto.Sta.	5171	3225	1978	1994
149876	Boston, Church Rd P.Sta.	5335	3435	1946	1970
152006	Dingley Resr Auto.Sta.	4774	2867	1985	1994
152426	Caldecott	4865	2932	1958	1971
155962	Manthorpe S.Wks Logger Sta.	5067	3164	1979	1995
163095	Oundle S.Wks Auto.Sta.	5038	2897	1981	1993
163469	Corby S.Wks Auto.Sta.	4906	2889	1981	1994
163918	Wittering Met.Office	5048	3032	1947	1986
164015	Wittering Met.Office	5043	3026	1984	1993
165129	Wisbech P.Sta.	5465	3102	1948	1971
165395	Crowland S.Wks Auto.Sta.	5246	3091	1978	1993
166869	Sutton Bridge	5476	3201	1978	1989
174062	Bedford 'B'	5049	2597	1980	1993
174566	Cardington Met.Office	5081	2463	1954	1979
175915	Silsoe	5091	2358	1951	1971
179624	Wyton Met.Office	5284	2745	1967	1993
186331	Broom's Barn	5753	2656	1984	1994
187228	Mildenhall Met.Office	5683	2778	1935	1968
188832	Honington	5888	2750	1969	1993
193359	Marham Met.Office	5737	3091	1951	1989

Gauge number	Site	Easting	Northing	First year	Last year
197430	March	5421	2967	1971	1981
199124	Marham Met.Office	5726	3094	1974	1993
206273	West Raynham Met.Office	5847	3245	1948	1968
208422	Horsham St Faith, Met.Office	6220	3131	1947	1956
215803	Hemsby Met.Office	6493	3162	1979	1995
221299	Felixstowe Met.Office	6286	2328	1921	1960
221992	Wattisham	6026	2514	1982	1995
224243	Cavendish	5801	2468	1980	1995
236428	Shoeburyness (Landwick) Met.Office	5961	1878	1978	1989
236466	Shoeburyness Met.Office	5948	1857	1980	1995
238097	Dagenham, Central Park Nursery	5499	1863	1961	1975
9000056	Ruskington	5091	3505	1978	1991
9000058	Ludford	5208	3893	1978	1994
9000059	South Witham	4929	3198	1978	1994
9000060	Keelby	5169	4098	1978	1994
9000066	Ravensthorpe	4681	2703	1978	1994
9000072	Ridds Farm	4938	3255	1977	1990
9000089	Stimpston Ave	4768	2616	1979	1994
9000090	Tugby	4760	3005	1977	1990
9000093	Cauldron Low	4058	3480	1985	1995

Thames catchment

Gauge number	Site	Easting	Northing	First year	Last year
242501	Hertford S.Wks	5338	2134	1952	1971
243131	Stansted Mountfitchet, S.Wks Auto.	5504	2243	1985	1995
243350	Stansted	5531	2226	1957	1995
245117	Southgate, Oakwood Park	5299	1952	1971	1987
245281	Walthamstow, Lowhall Farm Depot	5363	1881	1971	1981
245310	Hackney, Clapton Pond	5349	1860	1960	1976
246180	Camden Square	5291	1838	1881	1920
246211	London Weather Centre	5308	1816	1975	1995
246263	St James's Park	5298	1800	1973	1991
246327	Kensington Palace	5259	1801	1922	1973
246627	Mill Hill Cemetery	5231	1917	1961	1995
246690	Hampstead	5262	1863	1933	1995
246719	Stanmore, Uxbridge Rd	5155	1921	1942	1971
246738	Edgware, Chandos Park	5189	1911	1942	1973
246847	Brent Resr	5208	1870	1949	1995
247060	Ealing, Castlebar	5170	1819	1962	1975
247344	Northolt Met.Office	5099	1846	1947	1995
247449	Wood End Nurseries	5094	1813	1929	1973
247536	Heathrow	5077	1767	1947	1994
247669	Isleworth, Mogden S.Wks	5154	1753	1969	1995
248965	Rapsgate Resr Auto.Sta.	3996	2105	1985	1995
251530	Lechlade, St John's Lock Auto.Sta.	4222	1990	1985	1995
252449	Brize Norton, Met.Office SSER	4292	2067	1983	1993
253731	Little Rissington, Met.Office	4209	2191	1942	1975
254336	Eynsham Lock Auto.Sta.	4445	2087	1983	1995
256225	Oxford	4509	2072	1980	1993

Gauge number	Site	Easting	Northing	First year	Last year
256230	Osney Lock Auto.Sta.	4504	2058	1986	1995
259110	Bicester S.Wks Auto.Sta.	4581	2212	1985	1995
259480	Upper Heyford Met.Office	4513	2263	1928	1943
260991	Abingdon Met.Office	4479	1991	1943	1975
261021	Abingdon S.Wks Auto.Sta.	4493	1952	1986	1995
264270	Benson	4633	1909	1950	1995
266474	Marlborough, Salisbury Hill Auto.Sta.	4184	1686	1986	1995
268851	Chieveley S.Wks Auto.(RADAR) Sta.	4468	1739	1981	1995
271432	South Farnborough 'B'	4867	1544	1922	1995
271491	Camberley S.Wks Auto.Sta.	4862	1598	1981	1995
271975	Odiham Met.Office	4737	1494	1980	1995
272734	Bracknell, Beaufort Park Met.Office	4846	1664	1972	1995
275169	Maidenhead S.Wks	4893	1804	1944	1971
276539	Rothamsted	5132	2134	1952	1971
276540	Rothamsted No.2	5132	2134	1952	1971
277407	Radlett, Blackbirds S.Wks Auto.Sta.	5148	2002	1985	1995
277568	Aldenham School	5157	1972	1980	1992
278264	Bovingdon Met.Office	5007	2038	1954	1966
279502	Ruislip, Manor Farm Bowling Green	5090	1876	1958	1990
281186	Bordon Camp S.Wks Auto.Sta.	4804	1362	1981	1995
282290	Cranleigh S.Wks Auto.(RADAR) Sta.	5041	1393	1981	1995
284152	Hampton	5131	1695	1954	1974
284231	Broadfield	5263	1345	1951	1970
284324	Gatwick	5265	1407	1959	1995
284703	Burstow S.Wks Auto.Sta.	5305	1437	1981	1995
285630	Leatherhead, Elmer Wks Auto.Sta.	5159	1557	1981	1995
286392	Hogsmill Valley S.Wks	5194	1683	1961	1995
286405	Kingston, Canbury Gardens	5179	1700	1948	1976
287049	Kew Observatory	5171	1757	1886	1980
287052	Kew (Royal Botanic Gardens)	5185	1773	1981	1995
287059	Kew S.Wks	5197	1767	1967	1990
287203	Raynes Park P.Sta.	5237	1695	1961	1976
287283	Putney Heath Resr	5234	1737	1967	1995
287451	Chipstead, How Green Resr	5283	1581	1973	1995
287722	Purley, Oaks Depot	5321	1623	1965	1995
287764	Croydon Met.Office	5312	1633	1923	1955
287864	Beddington, New S.Wks	5299	1661	1972	1995
287909	Morden Hall	5261	1685	1960	1976
287946	Mitcham, London Rd Cemetery	5278	1701	1965	1985
289129	Greenwich	5387	1776	1954	1995

Southern England

Gauge number	Site	Easting	Northing	First year	Last year
290007	Cross Ness S.Wks	5486	1805	1966	1995
291241	Orpington P.Sta.	5459	1652	1963	1995
298019	West Malling Met.Office	5677	1553	1947	1968
301114	Manston	6335	1666	1936	1995
301621	Lympne Airport	6112	1355	1921	1954
302770	Canterbury S.Wks	6169	1597	1962	1973

Gauge number	Site	Easting	Northing	First year	Last year
307815	Playden, Scots Float	5933	1225	1963	1984
309038	Hastings	5809	1094	1979	1995
309902	Herstmonceux	5645	1099	1981	1992
320198	Tangmere Met.Office	4911	1064	1947	1956
321377	Thorney Island, Met.Office	4758	1026	1958	1975
322341	Cowplain, Greenfield Crescent	4691	1114	1987	1996
322485	Portsea: Eastney	4684	993	1950	1970
322487	Portsea: Eastney P.Sta.	4675	992	1987	1996
323138	Fareham, Peel Common S.Wks	4567	1035	1988	1996
331445	Calshot Met.Office	4489	1025	1920	1957

South-east England

Gauge number	Site	Easting	Northing	First year	Last year
336376	Boscombe Down Met.Office	4172	1403	1931	1995
336402	Larkhill Met.Office	4137	1447	1961	1979
339816	Porton Met.Office	4210	1366	1954	1979
346474	Hurn	4117	978	1954	1995
355363	Exeter Met.Office	3001	933	1947	1990
363474	Princetown	2584	741	1942	1993
368487	Mount Batten, Met.Office	2492	529	1930	1993
379758	Falmouth	1802	325	1886	1947
382430	Camborne Met.Office	1628	407	1980	1993
383478	St Mawgan	1873	642	1951	1993
395162	Chivenor 'B'	2496	1344	1950	1993
396384	Lundy: Stoneycroft	2133	1443	1980	1989
401005	Yeovilton RNAS Met.Office	3551	1237	1981	1993
403219	Northmoor P.Sta.	3332	1330	1946	1971
411686	Lyneham Met.Office	4006	1782	1947	1993
418120	Filton Met.Office	3600	1805	1937	1980
419869	Kingswood S.Wks	3743	1929	1979	1995

Wales (non-Severn catchment)

Gauge number	Site	Easting	Northing	First year	Last year
464675	Rhayader S.Wks	2979	2674	1980	1990
468345	Builth Wells, Cefndyrys SSER	3038	2530	1981	1995
473822	Lyonshall	3339	2576	1980	1994
489277	Pontsticill No.12	3060	2116	1937	1969
492325	Rhoose	3066	1677	1954	1995
497412	Penmaen	2531	1889	1981	1989
499324	Llanelli Filters	2516	2024	1940	1970
499582	Gorslas Resr SSER	2563	2147	1981	1995
508167	St Twynnells	1955	1969	1980	1989
508580	Pembroke Dock Met.Office	1952	2033	1948	1956
511956	Brawdy	1851	2248	1974	1992
517546	Aberporth Met.Office	2242	2521	1946	1995
532207	Anglesey: Valley Met.Office	2309	3757	1956	1995
532408	Salt: Holyhead Met.Office	2252	3832	1924	1955
547371	Moel-y-Crio	3194	3699	1982	1995
549026	Hawarden Met.Office	3342	3648	1947	1956
549210	Sealand Met.Office	3332	3701	1930	1945

Gauge number	Site	Easting	Northing	First year	Last year
North-west England					
551717	Cholmondeley	3552	3505	1945	1996
553563	Worleston S.Wks	3665	3574	1976	1985
558292	Chapel Resr Auto.Sta.	4069	3785	1985	1995
558489	Kinder Filters	4054	3880	1942	1996
559024	Arnfield Resr	4012	3972	1951	1970
560556	Sale, Carrington Lane	3765	3927	1950	1970
560854	Greenfold Resr No.1	3823	4261	1951	1970
560942	Holden Wood Resr No.2	3767	4224	1982	1990
564419	Ringway	3821	3849	1942	1995
564572	Trentabank Resr	3962	3712	1946	1996
564768	Prestbury S.Wks	3897	3782	1950	1969
565547	Dunham Massey S.Wks	3726	3875	1948	1996
567345	Speke Met.Office	3437	3820	1954	1976
567423	Aigburth (RTC)	3384	3852	1968	1991
568454	Aughton Met.Office	3394	4063	1980	1995
568594	Formby, Hightown P.Sta	3295	4045	1952	1995
574767	Nelson	3872	4384	1954	1995
575108	Accrington, Oak Hill Park	3764	4277	1951	1970
576634	Preston, Moor Park	3537	4311	1960	1995
577267	Squires Gate	3316	4316	1949	1990
586055	Levens, Bridge End	3474	4857	1952	1971
590602	Eskmeals Met.Office	3085	4931	1978	1995
592199	St Bees Head	2941	5143	1976	1986
592448	Seathwaite Logger Sta.	3235	5121	1980	1995
594201	Cornhow Tr.Wks SSER	3150	5222	1980	1995
595739	Aspatria	3154	5423	1982	1995
596013	Silloth Met.Office	3125	5537	1949	1960
603649	Spadeadam	3599	5720	1960	1970
606336	Carlisle 'B'	3384	5603	1961	1995
Scotland					
610122	Eskdalemuir Observatory	3235	6026	1910	1989
610123	Eskdalemuir Observatory SSER	3235	6026	1970	1995
615449	Moffat, Hydro Gardens Logger Sta.	3079	6063	1987	1996
621336	Eliock Logger Sta.	2797	6074	1982	1996
624033	Newtonairds Logger Sta.	2889	5799	1985	1995
624348	Lochrutton W.Wks SSER	2901	5743	1981	1995
627056	Upper Black Laggan Logger Sta.	2476	5769	1985	1995
627059	Black Laggan Logger Sta.	2469	5777	1983	1995
631269	Loch Fleet, Craigwhinnie SSER	2557	5698	1986	1995
632473	Kirriereoch Logger Sta.	2362	5871	1987	1996
637507	West Freugh Met.Office	2109	5546	1946	1975
645590	Prestwick Met.Office	2369	6261	1947	1993
646766	North Craig Resr SSER	2438	6412	1980	1995
652673	Carnwath SSER	2974	6464	1981	1995
654630	Mauldslie SSER	2808	6502	1983	1995
659049	Renfrew Met.Office	2508	6663	1946	1966

Gauge number	Site	Easting	Northing	First year	Last year
660285	Abbotsinch Met.Office	2480	6667	1936	1995
660629	East Kilbride SSER	2638	6535	1986	1995
675177	Machrihanish 'B'	1663	6225	1965	1989
691870	Fort William	2097	7734	1891	1904
691880	Ben Nevis Observatory	2170	7710	1885	1904
(gauge number invented by the author)					
713571	Kinlochewe	2025	8629	1960	1972
719008	Tiree: Met.Office No.1	999	7446	1954	1989
719010	Tiree: Met.Office No.2	999	7446	1957	1995
719395	Rhum: Kinloch	1402	7996	1961	1972
727288	Lewis: Stornoway Met.Office	1464	9332	1954	1995
736633	Benbecula: Airport	782	8555	1954	1995
753986	Strathy Logger Sta.	2839	9641	1986	1995
754402	Forsinain Logger Sta.	2906	9485	1986	1996
763886	Shetland: Lerwick Observatory No.2	4453	11397	1953	1989
763888	Shetland: Lerwick Observatory SSER	4453	11397	1957	1995
767475	Orkney: Kirkwall Met.Office	3483	10076	1947	1989
770765	Wick Airport	3364	9522	1948	1995
778575	Benmore Lodge Logger Sta.	2324	9121	1986	1995
779232	Corriemulzie Logger Sta.	2329	8955	1987	1996
788069	Dingwall Logger Sta.	2538	8593	1986	1995
795625	Mullardoch Dam	2223	8310	1962	1971
805708	Dalcross Met.Office	2766	8520	1980	1989
808493	Coignafearn Logger Sta.	2710	8178	1986	1995
811394	Kinloss Met.Office	3067	8627	1951	1995
817692	Aviemore Met.Office	2896	8143	1983	1995
823897	Rothes	3285	8497	1984	1994
827902	Keith S.Wks SSER	3433	8518	1982	1995
841496	Dyce Met.Office No.3	3877	8127	1946	1995
841720	Aberdeen Observatory	3939	8081	1886	1937
849814	Aberdeen, Mannofield Resr	3915	8042	1972	1995
859313	Mylnefield SSER	3339	7301	1980	1995
870623	Faskally SSER	2918	7599	1981	1995
885313	Leuchars Met.Office	3468	7209	1936	1995
887239	Loch Leven Sluices SSER	3171	6994	1980	1995
891986	Stronachlachar	2401	7103	1960	1968
892605	Loch Venachar SSER	2598	7063	1981	1995
894219	Stirling S.Wks SSER	2808	6935	1984	1995
899407	Turnhouse Met.Office	3159	6739	1948	1995
900175	Fairmilehead Logger Sta.	3249	6684	1986	1995
903638	Nunraw Abbey SSER	3594	6700	1983	1995
903798	Dunbar Logger Sta.	3672	6791	1969	1995
906423	Baddinsgill Resr SSER	3126	6554	1982	1995

Northern Ireland

927736	Omagh S.Wks	2441	3737	1971	1986
930761	Ardeemore SSER	2060	3807	1982	1994
932610	Strabane, Glen Rd	2353	3981	1985	1996

Gauge number	Site	Easting	Northing	First year	Last year
938575	Ballykelly Met.Office No.3	2624	4234	1946	1970
939063	Banagher, Caugh Hill	2663	4047	1984	1996
941654	Huntly S.Wks	3118	3467	1962	1971
947599	Seagahan Filters	2897	3382	1958	1967
947811	Armagh	2878	3458	1886	1970
953020	Broughshane Filters	3164	4089	1971	1982
955817	Aldergrove Met.Office	3147	3798	1926	1994
956927	Pomeroy Forest	2705	3724	1966	1985
959461	Toomebridge	2988	3905	1966	1984
962647	Coleraine, The Cutts	2854	4302	1966	1981
963676	Altnahinch Filters	3115	4238	1971	1994
968133	Belfast P.Sta.	3352	3769	1985	1994
969274	Hillsborough	3251	3577	1971	1981
969330	Hillsborough SSER	3233	3613	1987	1996
972770	Hare Island	3504	3492	1966	1985
977464	Newry Urban S.Wks	3091	3247	1965	1988
995505	Portora Sluice	2222	3453	1967	1986
996635	Castle Archdale Met.Office	2175	3587	1943	1955

Republic of Ireland

Gauge number	Site	Easting	Northing	First year	Last year
8000074	Clones	2500	3263	1960	1990
8000080	Malin Head	2422	4591	1961	1990

Index